TUNE INTO
HAPPINESS
FREQUENCY

YOUR BLUEPRINT FOR MENTAL
AND PHYSICAL WELLBEING

NATASCHA ENRIQUEZ

notionpress
.com

INDIA • SINGAPORE • MALAYSIA

ISBN 979-8-89066-776-2

Disclaimer

This book contains accounts of personal experiences that my clientele has shared with me over the years. These stories have been combined and given a different context, where appropriate, to maintain privacy and confidentiality. The core and outcome of each experience remains unaltered to keep the power of the story, but any details that may link an event to a particular person or situation are purely coincidental.

To Akin
My driving force and the love of my life!

To Alvaro
May you forever run wild and free!

Contents

CONTENTS

CONTENTS

CONTENTS

Why You Should Read This Book!

This book is all about you. It's an opportunity for you to explore the full potential of your mental and physical health and well-being. If you dream big enough, and you are ready to free yourself from the limiting beliefs that discomfort in body and mind is normal and unavoidable, then you are holding the blueprint for your personal Happiness Frequency, right here in your hands.

As you read this book, you will gain greater awareness. You'll be able to separate who you think you are, how you are supposed to feel, and what you should do from a truth that exists inside of you – you are the creator of your life and your life's experience.

As you read this book, you will develop practices to help you align with your goals, desires, and wildest dreams. Every time you learn something new, you will create new synaptic connections in your brain; the neurological tissue will physically be changed. The way you think, feel, and behave will shift, all because you created this change!

After you've read this book, you will have new tools to help you consistently maintain behaviors that are in line with your intentions. You'll have tools to help change scenarios on the fly, to facilitate new experiences. What's more, you will know how to create the biological and biochemical foundation for Happiness. Your lifestyle will be consciously optimized, and your mind and body will be primed to stay within your Happiness Frequency. Does this sound too good to be true? Are you wondering what the catch is? There is only one catch, but it's not so much a catch as it is a catalyst – nobody is going to do it for you. The power of choice is yours and yours alone.

The best part is that you don't have to be a scientist, you don't have to be a nutritionist, a yogi or a psychologist. You can make all the necessary changes to create the life of your dreams with the simple steps outlined in this book. You will read important physical and mental health facts and you will become aware of the intrinsic interconnection between the physical body, our endocrine system, the nervous system, our eating habits, and our mindset. Whilst this might sound like a lot of information, you will soon realize that after learning just a few scientific truths, you can draw the necessary connections and develop a roadmap for a sustainable, happier, and healthier life.

We live in a time of a consciousness revolution. We are aware that we need to make educated, conscious choices and changes to our lifestyles if we want to remain healthy in body and mind. There is knowledge all around us, and it is easily accessible, literally right at your fingertips. However, it is no longer enough to know, it is important to know how. Only if you are ready to turn knowledge into action can you expect to take advantage of this ever-expanding information.

It is a known phenomenon that most people wait for a crisis, disease, or life-threatening diagnosis before acting and changing something. But why wait for these tragic events when you hold all the knowledge and power in your hands? Deciding to change, right now, means believing in the future more than you believe in the past. It means being in love with life and embracing your full potential. It means to Tune into your Happiness Frequency!

I : Introduction

Why I do what I do!

I started my career in the Wellness and Fitness industry by studying Fitness Management in 2004. What led me on this path was an injury I suffered a few years prior, whilst preparing for my second-year dance exam for my Occupational Musical training. That was my first big career dream: becoming a musical dancer. But as for many other young, aspiring athletes and dancers, it was not meant to be. Repetitive jumps on hard flooring caused shin splints. Nevertheless, I didn't want to stop dancing, nor miss my exams. So, under the guidance of the school's physician, I continued training, high on pain medication. I eventually failed my exam (ironically, I passed dance but failed in acting and singing …). What then followed was a two-year period of chronic pain, single-minded diagnoses from several doctors, depression, and, simply put, pure agony.

At the age of 21, I was prepared to accept that I might need an artificial hip joint, vertebrae fusion of the lower spine, or that I might end up in a wheelchair. I only understood much later that the relatively common shin splint injury had caused me to be immobile, and because of a lack of strengthening and moving of my muscles, ligaments, and overall body,

I suffered from an impressive amount of serious structural issues. But there was nobody who explained this to me. It seemed that nobody I spoke to even understood this chain reaction. Back then, I just thought I was screwed!

After about two years of living with chronic pain and being quite impaired, I visited my hometown, which was a 6-hour train ride away, and met a friend, who had been a bodybuilder for some time. After listening to my story, he took me to his little gym in his basement, put me on the leg press (I think it was homemade), and started loading the plates. I remember thinking that he had completely lost his mind. The train ride to reach home had taken such a toll on me that I could hardly walk, and often needed assistance to get up. I remember one time crying desperately because my mother couldn't help me stand up from the sofa where I had laid down, and the pain was intolerable when I tried myself. I was weak and hopeless. At that time, I had very little experience with strength training and no understanding of the benefits of stability-enhancing training for rehabilitation. As dancers, we were told to avoid strength training so as not to build unnecessary, bulky muscle mass.... Fortunately, times have changed a bit.

However, back then in that little homemade gym, using the leg press, I knew within a few sessions that this was going to make the long-awaited difference in my life. I wasn't near fixed nor pain free, but I knew I was going to be fine eventually. So, whilst I studied Fitness Management, I continued to work on myself and rehabilitate my own body. I was my first Rehab client.

This event helped me to understand, through a very painful experience, that we often ignore the bigger picture when it comes to our body and mind. Injuries, pain, and mental distress are analyzed and treated in a singular manner, without investigating correlations and holistic cause and effect.

As I started my career, I continued to study anatomy and always enjoyed 'fixing' injured clients. Having gone through my own rehabilitation, I had a good intuitive understanding of what my patients' bodies needed to restore homeostasis of functional mobility and stability – which, in my experience, is the most important aspect of successful rehab training. Of course, it was also extremely rewarding and gratifying to help others to break their pain cycle. Empowering others to heal, whether physically or mentally, is still the greatest source of satisfaction for me. These clients also had an explicit urgency and need, and with that comes dedication. Naturally, the more intense a person's pain is, the more likely they are to stick to a program, to do the exercises, and to comply with the process.

Of course, I had many 'regular' clients as well. The average being men and women from ages 30 to 50, who realized that with advancing age they had to put in a little more effort to look (and feel) a certain way. They were people who had all the aches and pains that we seem happy to consider normal upon reaching a certain age. Parents who were lacking energy to be fully present for their children. Clients who got told by their physicians that they were approaching risky values for diabetes, high blood pressure, high cholesterol, etc. Whilst I considered all these issues as very valid and worrying, I soon realized that the level of perceived urgency varied greatly between my clients. Many times, I felt that I, or the money they paid me, was the only source of their motivation, and that there wasn't much intrinsic commitment. The aches and pains were normalized, and the desire to live a happier, healthier life wasn't high enough to commit to the required lifestyle changes. Because of this normalcy and the acceptance of this standard, I learned to become more selective with who I would take on as a client, trying to sort out those who were truly ready to commit. Fortunately, I never struggled to find enough clients, despite being on the expensive side as a trainer. But still, I always encountered draining situations, situations where I appeared to be the only source of motivation. Too many times I watched all the achieved gains disappear because of holiday seasons, dinners, and busy work schedules.

During this time, I had another realization – many people, if not most, shy away from aiming for excellence and happiness for themselves. It appears easier to be satisfied with the tiredness, the lack of energy, the onset of obesity and lifestyle diseases than to make the required changes. I wondered if it was a fear of failing, an inability, or a phobia to dream big – shying away from wanting to be different and, rather, wanting to blend into the unhealthy masses. I started to focus on goal setting with my clients, enabling them to be fully in charge of the process and to only commit to what they perceived to be necessary, realistic, and worthwhile. Whilst this was empowering for the clients, this shift in my coaching style was often frustrating for me, as many times I would have liked to see my clients aim higher and reach different outcomes. However, I understood that the process had to be client driven to foster greater commitment in the individuals.

Fast forward to 2018, whilst I was working at New York University in Abu Dhabi. I had the fantastic opportunity to work closely with the Director of Learning and Organizational Development. He encouraged me to pursue a Life Coaching certification, which I was contemplating doing, as I was wondering if that might finally give me the tools to instill intrinsic motivation in my clients. I am so grateful for the experiences and learnings during this time, as they really shaped my coaching methodology. My time at NYU was the essential early foundation for the Created Coaching methodology and this book, in so many ways that I cannot begin to list them all. Due to some unusual collaborations, the support of faculty members and researchers, as well as a healthy dose of my stubbornness, I even established the Sport and Wellness Science Lab and was able to conduct research with students, exploring the effects of short mindfulness interventions on the body, mind, and more.

To many, my career might appear scattered, as if I was moving between different professions, and yet to me, it is the only way and the only logical progression. I studied anatomy, physiology, nutrition, chemical principles of nutrients as well as physical and mental diseases, sport science and medicine, neuroscience, coaching techniques, eastern and western psychology and mind coaching, eastern and western movement and medicine principles, and quantum physics. Whenever I explored a new science, it quickly became apparent how interconnected and transferable all knowledge is.

I believe that there is a science missing, one that combines all the above to finally enable us to move away from our singular approach of treating and preventing diseases and illnesses of the body and mind. We know about the mind-body connection, both intuitively and through studies, however, we are not using this knowledge to our advantage. It is time that we learn the required tools to live conscious, happy, and healthy lives in body and mind.

It is time to take responsibility for our happiness and become the director of our story!

Yes, this is a new concept, and at first it might sound intimidating, like you'll have to study and research for years. But this book is here to change the way you think about your lifestyle, your mind and body, and about the value and importance you give to yourself.

By the time you finish this book, I hope that this way of thinking won't just be known to you; I want it to feel intuitive.

My wish for you is to aim high and succeed!

What you have read so far was the first chapter of my manuscript for quite some time. Everything I wrote is true, of course, and valid information. It describes a crucial point in my life that started my professional career and led me to where I am now. It gives you important details of my studies and the knowledge I collected over the years, which made me an expert in a few areas of physical and mental health science.

However, I've realized that I have been shying away from sharing my full truth with you, dear reader. I did this because I do not like to be defined by the other part of my story. However, there is no denying that it is the bigger reason, the 'THAT is why I do what I do'. When I began writing this book, I did not fully understand the importance of opening myself up to my own teachings. For me, it is highly uncomfortable to share and write about this. As I do, I feel I'm making this book about myself, like I'm whining and giving myself too much importance.... But hopefully, this is relevant for some of you to hear, helps you understand, and lets you connect more with this book. Here it goes.

I grew up as a single child with my mother and father. I had, and still have, three half-brothers from my father's first marriage; however, they lived in a different country and the relationship between them and my father had already been estranged and complicated.

I grew up feeling unsafe. I never knew when my father's mood would switch and he would turn from the father I adored as a little girl to an angry, raging, emotionally and verbally abusive man.

I grew up seeing my mother cry a lot. I grew up comforting my mother, who had nothing to give to my extremely strong-willed and manipulative father.

I grew up seeing a completely dysfunctional relationship. I grew up with parents who had few friends. I grew up with a father who would belittle and bad-mouth his relatives, what friends he did have, the relatives of my mother – basically everyone.

I grew up having to be strong. I was told by my father that that's how I should be – strong, independent, and always standing up for myself. I embraced that even more by watching my 'weak' mother suffer, incapable of protecting me.

I grew up longing for a big family, to have my brothers, to have people. But ultimately, I was alone.

I grew up with my father telling me about his affairs, his urge to get away from my mother, how my mother drove him crazy. I hated myself for understanding why her weakness disgusted him so much. I hated watching her suffer.

When my mother finally left my father, I crumbled. By that time, I hadn't spoken to my father for the better part of two years, despite living in the same house. My mother had always said that she stayed with him for my sake. When she left him, I was finally able to let go of the fear, the stress, and the panic. Looking back, I now understand that I had been operating in survival mode for quite some time, and I was now feeling the aftereffects. What followed was a depression that made it impossible for me to get out of bed in the morning.

I quit school when I was 17. I drank. I smoked. I engaged in all kinds of risky behavior. I was looking for help, but there was no one to help. I taught myself to stop feeling. I became cold. My way of relating with men was through emotionless, physical connection. I had no awareness of the damage I was doing to myself. I thought I was so strong but I was unbelievably weak. Even though I later began to work through my past experiences, I really didn't become fully aware of all the things I needed to unpack until I started my life coaching career. I am still constantly learning and working on myself. I have, however, learned to accept that this IS my life – the learning. The ongoing growth. I don't need to wait until I have achieved full awareness and wisdom to live my life to the fullest. I have learned to be less scared. I am practicing being vulnerable, but it is still hard.

To this day, as I am finally editing this first chapter, I do not yet know how to have a healthy relationship. I am learning, but I am often hijacked by my subconscious and self-sabotaging beliefs. I am trying to release the idea that I must always be strong. That I must always do everything alone. That I must never let myself be weak. And that love equals weakness. So, as I am writing this book, my personal, most challenging topics are the ones about paradigms and subconscious beliefs, things we'll of course be diving into later.

Being the director of your story

I could continue to share more about my situation today, that I am a single mother, that there are many days I struggle to make ends meet, the frustration of having to constantly operate on full speed to grow my business, the effort it takes to stay motivated and positive no matter what, and the challenge to be a present, patient mother – even when everything seems to go wrong. But none of this, including everything I shared about my past, actually matters!

The beauty of becoming the director of our story is that the past only matters by way of reminding us of who we no longer are.

It's a well-meaning warning about the behaviors and thought patterns that have gotten us to where we are, but no longer want to be. What I shared above is not who I am anymore, nor is it a past I want to empower to define me any longer. This is why, initially, I did not add this part of the chapter. It is no longer relevant. However, I do understand that it might help some readers to hear my full story and to relate how I am using my past to create a new, happy, satisfied future for myself and my son. When we are ready to take ownership and responsibility for the direction of our lives, the past merely serves as a memory of who we no longer are and enables us to redirect.

From the moment we wake up, we think thoughts. These thoughts, in turn, create our feelings and our emotions. This emotional experience becomes part of our physical experience and, eventually, who we are. Of course, I will explain this in more detail in this book.

For now, let us just be aware that most of us are busy repeatedly retelling the story of our past. You wake up and think, 'Oh no, I don't want to get up. I am tired' without taking the time to check in with your body and mind. Maybe you are, in fact, not tired. But you are too busy running your old program to notice.

You start thinking about all the things in your life (the past), the stress, and the worries. Someone cuts you off in traffic, and you think something like, 'Great, just what I needed'. You get to the office, thinking, 'I need coffee' (making yourself dependent), and whilst you are standing in the kitchen a co-worker asks, 'How are you?' You say, 'I am so glad you asked. I am so tired, I really need this coffee right now, and I hate Mondays, and you keep recounting all these thoughts and feelings that are based on experiences of the past.

In this way, we are just like outdated computers. Throughout our life, we have uploaded data and programs, but we never take stock, delete old programs, or upgrade. We might add new software, but too often the old ones remain more prominent. And just as with an old computer, with a working capacity limited by its operating programs, we are also limited by our leftover, antiquated thought patterns and beliefs.

Research has found that our brain processes about 60,000 to 70,000 thoughts a day, and an astounding 90% of them are repetitive. Imagine the possibilities if we managed to eliminate all this leftover garbage and free our brains up to create new thoughts. Who could we become?

This book will empower you to do exactly this – take ownership of your thoughts and dream up, define and create your future. In addition, it will provide you with the tools to allow your body to rebalance itself and build the physiological foundation for happiness in body and mind. Because, as you will learn, the mind and body are intrinsically connected, giving us the ability to affect our well-being in many ways.

There is a wealth of knowledge available to us, but for many of us, the missing link is to bring it all together and consider our minds and bodies for what they truly are, an interconnected, fine-tuned masterpiece with infinite potential.

How to use this book

This book is for you, and this is your story.

To get the most out of this book, please keep in mind that it doesn't necessarily need to be used in a linear order; the individual chapters and exercises might not be in a way that is most relevant to you. There is not one exercise that must come first and no sequential step-by-step guide to ultimate physical and mental health and well-being.

You will probably find that there are topics that you're already familiar and comfortable with; these areas won't require much tweaking or adjustment. These chapters will likely make intuitive sense to you and appear logical. My suggestion would be to park these topics and the related exercises, revisiting them toward the end of your journey through this book. Instead, try focusing your energy on the topics that contain new and, therefore, more challenging information and exercises.

As a matter of fact, the chapters and exercises that are quite different from what you are already doing will give you the biggest outcome and change. The areas that are outside of your comfort zone will also take a while to become habitual, and, therefore, you can benefit from approaching them first. Let me give you an example. If someone tries to improve their physical appearance or lose some weight but is already working out five times a week, then it will be hard to achieve big results by simply streamlining their exercise routine and perfecting it. This person would have to improve in other areas, maybe nutrition or underlying hormonal issues, to trigger fast achievements. If you have a strong, established mindset practice and you are doing your breathing, your meditation, maybe even your goal-setting exercises, then you might not be able to create big changes in this area, but merely fine-tune your existing routine. However, this would be the topic you'd most probably gravitate to and want to work on first – it is already within your comfort zone.

So, as you're reading, find the exercises that you find most challenging and give them a go. Just remember, the more you feel challenged by it, the greater your outcome and reward will be. On top of that, the sense of achievement will be sweet.

You will find exercises throughout most chapters of this book. I highly recommend keeping a notebook at hand and finishing the exercises on the spot. They are designed to help you assess your current situation and make commitments to create your desired success story.

We are all completely different, our brains, our bodies, our minds, our souls, and our lifestyles. I invite you to make this book your own, to go on your own individual Created journey, and I would love to hear from you and about your experience with this book.

✳ **Key points**

- ✳ The past is the past: I only bring in my past to help give context, but aside from this, it is not relevant in my life today. This is the invitation I have for you, my reader – let the past exist purely as the past.
- ✳ Mind-body connection: The mind and body aren't the distinct entities we've been taught to view them as. It is the back-and-forth influence of one over the other that shapes our experience, and, further, it is our autonomous influence over each of these aspects that allows us to shape our experience.
- ✳ How to use this book: This book can be read from cover to cover, or it can be explored as more of a reference guide, jumping between chapters. Each chapter is written as a self-contained nugget for you to dive into as it becomes relevant to you.

The knowledge gap

Did you ever find it strange, or even worrisome, that you know much more about your line of work than you do about your own body? If you are a financial advisor, you know the ins and outs of the finance industry, you understand the cause and effect of financial climates and how major world events can affect the global financial market. You understand the connections between different events and their potential results. If you're a teacher, you know how to deliver the information of the curriculum in a way that enables your pupils to comprehend your teachings in a suitable and encouraging manner. You understand how to provide information to students with different characters, learning styles, and abilities. You know how to adjust your lessons depending on the moods of your class. A car mechanic knows how to maintain and repair a car engine and troubleshoot when something goes wrong. They may even be able to optimize performance by adding or removing parts – they can tell you how to get the best out of your engine.

In fact, many people know a fair bit more about their car than about the physiological and psychological mechanisms of their own body. Have you ever considered how much money, time, and effort you put into your car compared to the amount of effort, love, and care you put into your body? Of course, this does not apply to everyone. You might not own a car or have very little knowledge about your car. Like me. But I'm sure you understand my point.

Many of us have a limited understanding of our physiological and mental health, and even less when it comes to the connection between the two. Why is this? Whilst we learn biology in school and are taught about our organs, skeleton, and musculature, this is all rudimentary knowledge and often singular in nature, meaning we cover one topic at a time without looking at the interconnectedness. We don't study enough about the complex, clever design of our bodies and about the amazing ways in which they can heal and regenerate.

We're taught how the blood circulates through the arteries and veins, how it carries oxygen, but we aren't taught how to troubleshoot. So, what happens if the oxygenation of the body is limited? How do we recognize this? What would the symptoms be? Do we know how to increase the oxygen supply to the tissues, or do we need to immediately seek the advice of a doctor?

We learn how the food travels down the larynx through the esophagus into the stomach and how the food is being eliminated. But what happens if the gut and stomach are unhealthy, hurting, and causing secondary health issues? Could you recognize these secondary symptoms? Do you know how to solve this problem?

We know that the mind and body are connected, and we know that we should be taking care of both. But how can we do this on a daily basis and what does this connection of body and mind practically mean?

We know that the body requires nutrients and that we are supposed to eat five portions of fruits and vegetables a day. But do you know exactly how the different nutrients affect your physical and mental well-being? What does your gut health have to do with your mental health? Do you fully understand how exercise and movement can create a physiological and biochemical balance that can help you feel better in your body and in your mind? Do you know how you can use nutrition, movement, and wellness practices – such as mindfulness, meditation, and breathing – to better yourself and your physical and mental health, potentially reversing damage on a cellular level?

To be honest, I don't know why many of our societies have developed in the way that they have, losing the connection and knowledge about our own engines. I can speculate, however, and I assume that laziness and convenience have played a role. It is always easier to be told what to do and to hand over responsibility to those we consider experts. At the end of the day, you can't know everything about everything, right? Our extremely busy lifestyles are certainly not helping the matter; many of us feel overwhelmed with the simple, everyday tasks we must juggle.

Maybe you are taken aback by my frankness, but I am here to empower you to change and to make educated choices about your own life; this can only happen when we are ready to take responsibility.

Whatever the reasons for our lifestyle behavior and health unconsciousness, it doesn't really matter. What matters is that we accept that there is a huge knowledge gap and that we are going further and further in a dangerous and unhealthy direction. We are disconnected from our physical and mental bodies and have lost the connection to ourselves.

A fundamental flaw of our lifestyles is that we have developed in a way that has distanced us from our natural, humane lives. The toxicity and stress levels that our bodies and minds are exposed to have multiplied dramatically over the past centuries, especially since the industrial revolution. The lives that we are leading now are severely challenging to our physical and mental health. A hundred and fifty years ago, it was ok to go about your everyday life and not to be an expert in human health because the food you had available was naturally organic and seasonal. The stress you were exposed to was natural: episodes of high, often life-threatening, stress were followed by mental decompression times with your family, without constant electronic pollution and visual, auditory stimuli. Life was simple. Tough, but simple. Doctors were there to treat actual diseases. Yes, the life expectancy was lower, people died earlier, and often by causes we wouldn't die of anymore. But I would argue that their quality of life (except of course for disasters, war, etc.) was much higher. Further, people were able to perceive happiness, to actually feel happy about the small things. Thanks to modern health science, we are now able to prolong life expectancies, but our bodies are exposed to much more stressors and toxicity. This leads to a variety of new physical and mental health concerns that we, the individuals, need to learn to prevent, manage, and treat.

There is great confusion about the difference between lifestyle management and disease management. Let me clearly establish my opinion. Medical doctors are the experts on diseases. I am not someone to slash and blame the medical system, pharma industry, etc. I am here to tell you that we must take responsibility for our own health; doctors are not the ones to tell us how to live healthier lives. They are not to blame for our failure to better understand our own bodies and our inability to protect our systems from the unnatural lifestyles we are leading. Medical research is busy catching up with new diseases and finding cures and treatments. Let them do their job, and you do yours – taking care of YOU!

In our modern societies, with the disconnect from our natural lifestyle and the presence of all the stress, toxic food, and environment, it is paramount to develop a deeper understanding of the functions of our immune system, stress regulation, cellular renewal, nutrient supply, physiological exercise response, and hormone/ neurotransmitter functions. We must understand the effect of what we put into our bodies and how it is used to sustain and build our bodies of the future. We need to understand the mind-body connection thoroughly, and be able to troubleshoot any imbalances. We can no longer afford to give the responsibility away and simply expect to be told what to do when it's already too late.

The good news is that we are living in an exciting time of a well-being revolution. We are being encouraged to ask questions and not simply accept traditional behaviors at face value. There is a collective movement toward healing, toward connection, and toward self-love that is driven by the desire to be better, happier, and self-aware. Many people no longer settle for being alright. We don't accept statements such as, 'Well, we turned out ok' when discussing different parenting styles anymore. We acknowledge that mankind is, in fact, not ok, in the presence of war; cruelty; depression and anxiety numbers; starvation; hunger; greed; and poverty. We are waking up to the fact that it is ok to want more than ok. We are longing to reach our full potential as intelligent, intuitive, soulful human beings. Yet there is still the knowledge gap that prevents us from fully utilizing the interconnectedness of our bodies and mind.

Sounds daunting? Well, let me tell you the benefits of stepping into your responsibility, and subsequently, into your full potential.

Aside from leading a happier, healthier, more fulfilled life that you can truly enjoy, you will finally have greater control of your own health. You will no longer depend on the expertise of others but be enabled to make educated decisions about your well-being and your physical and mental happiness. Taking responsibility for your own physical and mental health, as well as your lifestyle, will be the most empowering step you will ever take.

In this book, you will learn the necessary knowledge about body, mind, soul, nutrition, movement, and how they are all connected. You will discover and create your own individual path to happiness. You will also learn about the importance of goal setting and how you can prioritize yourself even in busy times.

Let's go!

✶ Key points:

- ✶ The knowledge gap: People know a great deal about their profession and their passions, but what about their own bodies? In modern society, it has been normalized to outsource the responsibility of knowledge regarding our own well-being to doctors and other medical professionals.

* Life expectancy and life quality: We're living longer these days, but due to constant stressors, toxicity levels, and a lack of ability to feel smaller experiences of happiness in our modern lives, the quality of our lives is called into question.

* The doctor and the patient: While doctors are an incredible resource, it is important we get involved with ourselves and our own well-being, learning what activities and foods we need to help us feel a more stable sense of contentment in our day-to-day. This is what it means to take responsibility and discover our full potential.

* What to expect from this book: In this book, we'll work to bridge this knowledge gap and explore things such as nutrition, movement, goal setting, and how they're all connected to help you find your personal path to happiness. Let's go!

II : Brain Buster vs Brain Booster

Inside our heads is an astonishing living organ, which weighs about 1.5 kg and consists of billions of tiny cells. It enables us to sense the world around us, to think and to talk. The human brain is the most complex organ of the body, and arguably the most complex thing on earth.

It consists of many nerve cells, its building blocks, connected in networks. There is a constant state of electrical and chemical activity, even when we are asleep. The brain can see, feel, sense pain and danger, and coordinates our movements and bodily functions; in short, the brain coordinates our survival. The brain does a lot, and like many other parts of our body, it doesn't come fully formed but develops gradually. In fact, the brain never stops changing and developing.

Of course, the brain can also get injured, and it definitely experiences stress. In this chapter, we'll look at why this is and how this is, touching on some of the hormonal mechanisms that can lead to anxiety and chronic stress – as many of us feel at times.

I'm not about to give you a full crash course in Neuroscience over the next few pages, nor will either of us fully understand the brain at the end of this chapter. But we will explore some of the brain's functions and hormonal responses related to stress, as well as the concept of neuroplasticity and how we can use it to create a sustainable mindset shift and increase our sensations of happiness and well-being. We will get a better understanding of how we can boost our brain's ability to produce the happy hormones that will prove an important ally in helping us tune us into our Happiness Frequency.

 ## What is stress?

Stress, a word most people are uncomfortably familiar with. Though we feel it in varying degrees and frequencies, we all feel it, it's always there. You might even be thinking, 'I'm reading this book to be happier, why are we talking about stress?' Well, before we learn how to tune into our happiness frequency, we first need to do some groundwork. If we are to work on our mindset and beliefs, we first need to understand our current perceptions and how we ended up where we are right now. Because of this, what better way to start than with a bit of biology and a deeper understanding of what stress actually is? What really happens to the body and brain when we are stressed? Most importantly, why do we get so stressed?

We all experience stress, worries, and even anxiety. We often use phrases like, 'I am so stressed', 'This is freaking me out', 'I need to relax', or 'Calm down!' You might have suffered from more severe forms of stress such as a panic attack, constant fatigue, sleeplessness, digestive problems, headaches, body pain, elevated heart rate and blood pressure, etc. Even if not, you have most probably experienced physiological and psychological responses and symptoms to stress. We are becoming increasingly aware of the detrimental effects stress can have on our lives. 'Wellness' interventions, meditation, mindfulness, spa treatments, sound healing, and healing retreats are all becoming popular interventions for the stressed individual.

When we experience stress, rather, when the brain perceives a situation as stressful, our body reacts with a hormonal response in the form of releasing cortisol, epinephrine – also known as adrenaline – and other stress hormones. This cascade of hormones creates a burst of energy and activates the 'fight-or-flight' response, which enables us to respond to real or perceived danger.

This reaction, together with the direct actions of the autonomic nervous system, causes changes in the body's metabolism. Heart rate, blood pressure, and respiration rates increase, blood vessels in the arms and legs dilate, and muscle tension increases. Digestive processes are interrupted and change as the body releases glucose and fatty acids into the bloodstream to provide energy to the muscles, directing blood flow away from any nonessential functions. This physiological stress response is fast, efficient, and designed to help us respond quickly and effectively to any dangerous and threatening situation. It was, and still is, paramount for human survival.

There is just one big problem. The levels of stress, with all their severe physical and mental symptoms – particularly present in societies that are rarely exposed to actual life-or-death threats – are higher than ever and still rising. How can it be that those with the lowest dangers to their physical existence have the highest rates of burnout, anxiety, stress-related fatal diseases, and even suicide?

Whilst our fight-or-flight response causes reactions in the body, the brain is the key organ that recognizes, evaluates, and defines a stressful and threatening situation. Instrumental parts include the hypothalamic-pituitary-adrenal (HPA) axis, the amygdala, and parts of the prefrontal cortex. The amygdala, Latin for 'almond', is the brain structure that detects stress and signals for the HPA axis to respond and, accordingly, signal the rest of the body. It is the integrative center for emotions, emotional behavior, and motivation. The amygdala recognizes emotional and biological stressors, as well as external and internal stressors. Interestingly, aside from its crucial role in the fight-or-flight reflex, it also plays a pivotal role in our memory function.

The amygdala shares a direct connection with the prefrontal cortex, the control center of the brain. Here, the emotional response to stress can be regulated. The prefrontal cortex is a big region in the front of the brain. It helps to control our thoughts, actions, and all emotional responses to stress.

It is important to know that the prefrontal cortex is only fully developed by the age of twenty-one, with some recent literature even estimating it to be twenty-five years of age. Whilst we can regulate emotions before we reach this age, the processes are different and more rudimentary. The prefrontal cortex learns emotion regulation from experiences and previous events. Like all parts of the working brain, it continually develops and adapts, and can even be altered in its sensitivity to stress. That means that everyone's prefrontal cortex has a different stress threshold, based on age and experiences. Pre-existing stress levels factor into this as well.

The amygdala is part of what is called the 'downstairs brain', often referred to as the primitive or reptilian brain. This brain section also contains the brain stem and the limbic brain. This instinctive part of our brain is well developed from birth and is responsible for all basic functions of survival, such as breathing, blinking, heart beating, fear responses, and digestion. All mammals and even amphibians have an amygdala or a similar brain structure that recognizes danger in an irrational manner. The downstairs brain is not under our conscious control; however, we can influence the way we respond to perceived threats, by slowing down, taking deep breaths, and refocusing our thoughts. These simple steps can allow the prefrontal cortex to take over from the irrational amygdala.

Research has shown that we can even affect the size of the amygdala. It has been found that the amygdala is physically smaller in expert meditators. In general, the amygdala seems to react less to negative events as we get older. It still responds when there is a real threat but is less likely to get fired every time there is a lightly stressful situation. This might help us to maintain greater emotional stability. However, this natural progression is hindered in the presence of chronic stress.

What happens when we snap?

You can probably recall a situation when you, a friend, a family member, or maybe a colleague completely lost it. They might have shouted, cried, become verbally abusive, shut down, were unable to listen to anything that was said, acted in an irrational manner, and were effectively out of control. This is called an amygdala hijack. This term was first introduced by Daniel Goleman in his book: *Emotional Intelligence: Why it can matter more than IQ*, 1995.

During an amygdala hijack, the amygdala overrides control of a person's ability to respond to a perceived threat in a logical and rational manner. It hijacks the prefrontal cortex. The reaction becomes a purely emotional response to stress and causes us to lose control of our emotions. This results in sudden outbursts and is often followed by thoughts such as, 'what was I thinking?' Fact is, we are not thinking during an amygdala hijack and are acting solely based on our primal survival instincts. The amygdala initiates the fight-or-flight response before the cortex has had a chance to regulate it.

In the case of mild or moderate threats, the frontal lobes can normally overwrite the amygdala, but if a threat is perceived as severe, a hijack occurs. An undesired, immediate result of this is a depreciation in the working memory. We can 'no longer think straight'. A hijack causes us to narrow our thinking, to basically think with 'tunnel vision'. We can no longer see more than one solution to a threat, and that solution is our fight-or-flight response.

Many people express that they cannot think clearly and feel like their brain has gone foggy when they are emotionally overwhelmed or distressed.

This is, in fact, true if there is no contribution of the prefrontal cortex. Hijacks are often mistakes; they are sudden, emotional, negative outbursts to a situation that does not warrant resulting extreme reaction. However, psychological threats such as pressures and stressors of our modern lifestyles – such as work, relationships, anger, aggression, anxiety, and fear – can contribute to more frequent amygdala hijacks.

The symptoms of an amygdala hijack are the same as the onset of our fight-or-flight response:

- rapid heart rate
- clammy skin
- dilated pupils to improve vision for faster responses
- sweating
- goosebumps on the skin
- increased blood sugar levels for immediate energy
- contracted blood vessels to allow the body to redirect blood to major muscle groups
- airways expand to utilize more oxygen.

Unsurprisingly, a hyper-sensitive amygdala is associated with a variety of mental health conditions, specifically those involving anxiety. Fear and avoidance, which are common and underlie most anxiety disorders, can be related to an overactive amygdala. It has been reported that hyperactivation in the amygdala was frequently observed in individuals with social anxiety disorders and certain phobias. Greater amygdala activation and heightened emotional responses have also been observed in people experiencing panic disorder, posttraumatic stress disorder, and obsessive-compulsive disorder.

From developmental studies and research, it appears that the amygdala is particularly sensitive to stress in the early years. Being exposed to early life trauma or childhood mistreatment and neglect is now believed to have a significant effect on our stress response in later life. Experiencing childhood adversity also seems to result in long-lasting structural and functioning changes in the amygdala, in turn affecting the hormones involved in a hijack. The threshold for emotional reactions in children is lowered because of the repeated sensitization of the amygdala circuits. This may result in a heightened sensitivity to stressors and an increased activation of neural circuits.* In summary, it can be assumed that negative childhood experiences can lead to increased amygdala hijacks, overreactions to stress, and difficulties regulating emotions throughout life.

Aside from childhood causes, chronic stress also plays a crucial role in the adequate functioning of the fear circuits in the brain. Chronic stress can reduce the function of the

---

*   Tor D. Wager, Matthew L. Davidson, Brent L. Hughes, Martin A. Lindquist, Kevin N. Ochsner, Prefrontal-Subcortical Pathways Mediating Successful Emotion Regulation, Neuron, Volume 59, Issue 6, 2008, Pages 1037-1050, ISSN 0896-6273, https://doi.org/10.1016/j.neuron.2008.09.006.

hippocampus and the prefrontal cortex, the regions of the brain that can inhibit and regulate our stress responses.

What is chronic stress?

Stress is a normal part of life, and our bodies and brains are well equipped to deal with stressful episodes if adequate time for rest and recovery is provided in between. Chronic stress occurs when the brain is exposed to stressors with such frequency or intensity that the autonomic nervous system cannot activate the relaxation response, resulting in a constant state of physiological arousal. The amygdala, the fear center of the brain, is constantly activated. Cortisol levels remain elevated, which will eventually lead to digestive issues, sleep disturbance, and weakening of the immune system.

In addition, it has been found that when one part of the brain is constantly activated, other parts of the brain may not have enough energy to carry out their respective duties. Our brains are made up of gray matter and white matter. Whilst gray matter is used for decision-making and problem-solving, white matter is used to connect different regions of the brain to communicate and transfer information. During times of chronic stress, less gray matter is being built. The resulting imbalance in gray and white matter production can result in permanent changes to the brain structure. During this restructuring, the overall volume of the brain remains roughly the same.

Chronic stress can cause areas of the brain that are associated with emotions, metabolism, and memory to shrink, even in otherwise healthy individuals.

Chronic stress also makes us more likely to suffer brain shrinkage when we are exposed to isolated episodes of intense stress, meaning that we may be less equipped to deal with future stressors. In short, we are less resilient!

The above-described white and gray matter imbalance is also thought to play a significant role in the development of mental illnesses. It appears that excess myelin in certain areas of the brain interferes with the timing and balance of signaling and communication within the brain. Further, chronic stress negatively alters hippocampal function and, therefore, impacts memory, spatial memory, memory consolidation and memory transfer. It may even kill newly produced neurons in the hippocampus. Whilst the formation of new neurons does not seem to be affected, research shows that new neurons produced during periods of stress are more likely to die within one week.

How can we increase resilience and train the prefrontal cortex?

I know, we've discussed a lot of new terms and have gotten a bit deep into some biological processes. If your head is spinning, just stay with me, I promise you'll be glad to have this little biology crash course. Not only does it support concepts further on in the book, but the knowledge itself offers a unique focal point that can potentially help us through some challenging times.

This book is all about giving you control of your physical and mental well-being. It's about heightening your awareness of psychological and physiological processes and enabling you to make conscious decisions. When it comes to stress, you might, of course, not be able to eliminate all stressors from your life. However, you can gain greater control over your responses if you know your subconscious triggers. You will find more interesting lectures in the chapters about paradigm shifts, how our thoughts create our reality, and childhood vs adult trauma.

In this section, we will talk about simple, yet super effective, practices to prevent amygdala hijacks and increase your prefrontal cortex control. Please note that these techniques will not be effective if you wait for a moment of high stress or an amygdala hijack to try them for the first time. They need to be practiced and reinforced when you are reasonably calm to enable you to use them as a defense when needed. It is like competing in martial arts; it takes practice – in a relaxed, structured, and controlled environment – prior to meeting your opponent. If you have the tools, you can use them in the same structured, calm manner to defend your peace and calm state of mind.

1. Emotional Intelligence

Goleman, who, as mentioned earlier, was the first to popularize the term 'amygdala hijack', suggests that we must increase our emotional intelligence to build resilience. Five basic competencies that help us raise our EQ are self-awareness, self-regulation, motivation, empathy, and social skills.

Self-awareness: Being self-aware is the ability to <u>recognize a feeling</u> as it is happening. To prevent the amygdala from overriding rational thought, we must identify an emotional response and manage its control over the situation. Self-awareness is the skill to distinguish between accurate and inaccurate expressions of emotions.

Self-regulation: To be able to self-regulate means that we can <u>manage emotions</u>. It is the ability to connect or disconnect and engage or disengage from an emotion depending on its relevance to a situation. If we can self-regulate, we can respond logically with cognitive thought, as opposed to reacting emotionally without forethought. An emotionally intelligent individual can recognize when a hijack is coming and attempt to prevent an undesired reaction.

Motivation: An aspect of emotional intelligence is to strive to satisfy our intrinsic motivation in work and other activities, regardless of external incentives. This means that we are <u>connected to our goals</u> and have a clear understanding of what drives us and satisfies us, even during challenging times.

Empathy: If we are empathetic, we can <u>recognize emotions in others</u>. We can be understanding, aware of, and sensitive to others' feelings and work to utilize this ability to manage our own emotions, promote good emotions, as well as come to a positive result during a moment of conflict.

Social skills: <u>Interpersonal communication</u> is an important part of emotional intelligence. Good social skills equal good conflict-resolution skills. Thus, in times when a conflict may arise, those with strong social skills can react and respond to others in a positive way and defy stressful situations.

2. Mindfulness

It is probably of no surprise that Mindfulness is another important technique we can utilize to prevent amygdala hijacks. Personally, I would even say THE most important. Mindfulness is the ability to be fully present in the moment, to experience and feel authentically, and to be aware of oneself. Mindfulness certainly employs similar techniques to the EQ competencies as proposed by Goleman, and in that regard also increases emotional intelligence.

The beauty of mindfulness is that we can turn any activity in our day-to-day life into a practice, starting with brushing your teeth in the morning or having a shower. The next time you find yourself performing these typically mundane tasks, take a few moments to focus your full attention on your senses and experiences. How does the toothpaste taste? How does the shower gel smell? What is the temperature of the water? How does the toothbrush feel against your teeth and gums, how does the water pressure feel on your skin? How do you feel at this moment? What can you hear? What can you see? That first sip of coffee in the morning, smell it, taste it, see it, feel it! I am not saying that you must do this with all your daily activities; I simply want to demonstrate how easy it is to practice mindfulness. And if all fails, the best exercise is to focus on your breathing – you're already an expert at breathing.

Are you still not convinced? What if I told you that more isn't more, but less is? Our brain is wired to move on and change topics, it is quite fickle. So, practicing mindfulness for a minute is already a great and impactful achievement. Use a short task to practice daily and use a minute of mindful breathing a few times throughout your day to help the brain take a mini break and reset – simple, short, yet super effective! Mindfulness helps us to be more connected to the present moment and to be more engaged in our responses.

3. Managing stress exposure

Managing our overall stress exposure may very well be the best way to lower the risk of amygdala hijacks. Becoming aware of our own individual stressors and triggers is an important and useful exercise. Many, initially small, triggers can turn into a big problem over time. Other times, we are hijacked by sudden onset situations. Make a note of everyday stressors that turn into chronic stress to help identify ways to manage them. Effective stress management can include immediate relievers such as breathing exercises, tapping (EFT – Emotional Freedom Technique), or movement. General health habits such as exercise, meditation, and journaling can also be utilized to manage stress. Again, it is important to develop and establish a repertoire of destress exercises when we are relatively calm, to make sure these techniques are available to us when we are unsettled.

Amygdala hijack first aid

Whilst getting ourselves equipped with preventative measures, there will be times when amygdala hijacks do occur. Below are some hijack first aid exercises that can help cope with the situation.

Name the emotion: Recognizing and naming the emotion that is predominant can help give control back to the frontal lobes since this requires the use of language and analysis. Even simply stating 'I am mad' could be enough to make this feeling less intense and bring back a rational mindset.

6-second rule: Delaying any kind of response for about six seconds could prevent the amygdala from taking control and putting forward an emotional reaction. Whilst delaying the response, this time could be used to think about something positive or to focus on breathing. It is also a good idea to have a positive thought 'ready', like a mantra for you to repeat. My personal go-to is, 'I am safe'. I often advise clients to have an object, such as a piece of jewelry, that they use to connect to their positive thoughts.

Breathing: Breathing is a powerful tool during a heightened situation as it can trigger the parasympathetic nervous system (more information below) and bring about a calm bodily response. Taking control of the breath in stressful situations can allow thoughtful decisions that aren't driven by the triggered emotions of the moment. To quickly activate the parasympathetic nervous system, try exhaling for double the count of your inhale, e.g. inhale for a count of three and exhale for a count of six.

Change the setting: Getting up and moving around in a stressful situation forces your brain to reactivate its thinking part to assess the new surroundings. Taking some time out from a stressful situation if you are feeling out of control can also help to get a better hold of your emotions and see things from a rational perspective.

Share the mental load: When feeling a lot of emotions, sharing feelings with a trusted person can split the mental load and help our amygdala feel less threatened; it may even help the individual feel safe. In addition, the use of language in highly emotional situations encourages the use of the thinking part of the brain.

Amygdala hijacks are not preventable in every situation, and it is realistic to expect setbacks. However, when they do occur, there is a lot of learning and insight we can gain from them. After one has occurred, once you're feeling relaxed and settled again, take some time to acknowledge the feelings you experienced, what caused the hijack, and maybe even the reasons as to why this certain situation was a trigger. Decide if this is still a valid stressor in your present life or if you were, in fact, hijacked by an emotional response that belongs to the past. Again, you will find more information and exercises on this very important topic in other chapters of this book.

Parasympathetic and Sympathetic nervous system

As you have probably come to understand by now, stress is complex. Whilst we are aware of the multitude of effects stress has on us, and unfortunately often experience the different ways stress can impact our lives, we do not use this knowledge to our advantage. How do we do this? Well, the great advantage of a highly complex stress response is that there is a wide range of subsequent coping methods. We can tackle stress on a physiological and psychological level, re-creating calmness in the body as well as in the mind. No matter which system we choose to work on first, it will, in turn, affect the other system.

As mentioned above, the hypothalamus, more precisely the HPA axis, plays an important role in our stress response. This part of the brain acts like a command center and communicates with the body through the autonomic nervous system, which controls our involuntary bodily functions – blood pressure, heart rate, breathing, and constriction/ dilation of major blood vessels and bronchioles. The autonomic nervous system consists of the sympathetic and the parasympathetic nervous system. You can imagine the sympathetic nervous system like the gas pedal in your car. In case of perceived danger, it activates the fight-or-flight response in the body by providing the energy required to respond. The parasympathetic system, however, acts like the brake and promotes the 'rest and digest' response that calms us and restores our body's energy levels after the danger has passed.

Epinephrine, also known as adrenaline, is the initial hormone to trigger an immediate response of the hypothalamus. This reaction will help you survive sudden danger, such as an oncoming car on the road. As epinephrine levels decline, the hypothalamus will then activate the HPA axis. The HPA axis relies on a variety of hormonal signals to keep the sympathetic nervous system, the gas pedal, activated. If the amygdala is not regulated by the frontal lobes, the hormonal signals will prompt the adrenal glands to release cortisol, causing the body to stay in a high-alert stress response. Again, the immediate stress response will be the same, whether the stressor is an immediate life-threatening situation or an emotional stressor. However, the prolonged perception of stress, or an amygdala hijack, can be a result of previous trauma, prior events, adverse childhood experiences, or chronic stress.

If we cannot find a way to pull the brakes on stress, the HPA axis remains activated and we will experience tremendous negative effects on our physical and mental health. Persistent epinephrine surges can damage blood vessels and arteries, increase blood pressure, and raise the risk of strokes and heart attacks. Elevated cortisol levels cause physiological changes that help to replenish the body's energy reserves that are rapidly depleted during a stress response. However, they will inadvertently cause a buildup of fat tissue and weight gain, as it increases appetite and encourages the storage of unused nutrients as fatty deposits.

Stress that is left untreated and unresolved will contribute to many physiological health problems. Here are just a few reasons why we need to eliminate as much stress as possible from our lives:

- Stress can make you feel hot, sweaty, and jittery.
- Stress causes digestive problems.
- Stress can make you irritable, irrational, and angry.

- Stress affects our memory and working brain capacity.
- Chronic stress can lead to mental health problems such as depression and anxiety disorders.
- Stress causes sleep issues and may lead to insomnia.
- Stress decreases the immune system.
- Stress increases the risk of type II diabetes.
- Chronic stress causes weight gain.
- Chronic stress increases blood pressure and may increase the risk of heart attacks and strokes.

The vagus nerve: the stress-fighting superhero!

I know you might feel a little overwhelmed, but there is good news, and then more good news after that. Just as our bodies are designed to fight and run, so too are they designed to relax. All we have to do is tap into this natural ability we all have.

The vagus nerve is the main component of the parasympathetic nervous system and makes up around 75% of it. It oversees a vast array of body functions, including control of mood, heart rate, breath rate, and digestion. The vagus nerve is an important connection between the brain and the gastrointestinal tract and sends information about the inner organs back to the brain via afferent nerves.

If we engage in vagus nerve activating activities, we can strengthen this important part of our rest-and-digest response and, in turn, increase our resilience. The techniques mentioned above are all helpful, but breathing has a particularly great effect on the vagus nerve. This is because the parasympathetic nervous system actively controls the breath. Out of the autonomic nervous system functions, breathing is the one we can easily take conscious control over. Whilst we can theoretically also affect our heart rate, and even our digestive system, this requires quite diligent practice. Connecting to our breath, however, altering the length and depth, is easily accessible. Engaging in a breathing exercise, even just for a minute, will immediately activate the parasympathetic nervous system. Whilst the parasympathetic and the sympathetic nervous system can be switched on simultaneously, activating a physiological rest response will always have great benefits.

It is important to understand that even if we manage to prevent an amygdala hijack, a panic attack, or chronic stress through a conscious activation of the parasympathetic nervous system, our psychological reasons for stress have not miraculously disappeared. However, if we are in a constant state of fight-or-flight and amygdala activation, we can simply not think straight and will not be able to effectively work through our past traumas and experiences. On top of this, there are the severe physical risks associated with stress, as mentioned above. Hence, we can relax the body first, to then work on relaxing the mind.

Taking conscious care of our vagus nerve is important. In cases of prolonged chronic stress, the vagus nerve may lose its ability to switch the parasympathetic function of rest and recovery back on. Known as vagal dysfunction, this condition puts us at risk of stress-related health problems.

How can we support healthy vagus nerve function?

What we really want to focus on is the tone of the vagus nerve. The vagal tone represents the activity of the vagus nerve. Increasing our vagal tone activates the parasympathetic nervous system, and having a higher vagal tone indicates that our body can relax faster after a stressful event. Research has verified that there is a positive correlation between high vagal tone, positive emotions, and good physical health. In short, an increased vagal tone means improved physical and mental health and resilience.

Our vagal tone can be measured by tracking certain biological markers, such as heart rate, breathing rate, and heart rate variability (HRV). If you have a smartphone or sport watch, it might give you a stress index, which is basically your HRV. HRV is the variability of the time interval between the heartbeats. Picture the line of an electrocardiogram that measures that heartbeat. The small pulses in between the large heart rate spikes represent the variability between the heartbeats. Again, these are primarily markers of physiological stress, but you can now use your advanced understanding to induce physiological relaxation, prior to working on mastering significant mindset changes or if you are about to face challenging situations.

In my coaching, I use a wonderful methodology called Horse-Guided Empowerment (Marzmethod). In this technique, we use the presence of horses to bring our clients into a more relaxed state. It has been scientifically proven that the electromagnetic field of the horse's heart and their beneficial

HRV helps to optimize our HRV and, in turn, allows us to stop our fight-or-flight response. I have witnessed many times how a client visibly relaxes into a calmer mindset within minutes of being in the paddock.

But even without a horse in your backyard, there are many great techniques to increase our vagal tone. As I promised in the beginning, I will explain the interconnectedness between body and mind from many different angles. This makes writing this book challenging at times; I am aiming to provide an understandable structure, rather than overwhelming you with a large continuous body of text, and I am conscious that this chapter on stress is already getting a lot longer than anticipated (I can't say I'm surprised – there's a lot to go over). Because of this, however, you'll likely notice connected and recurring information in different parts of this book, as the topics weave and naturally elaborate as we go. For example, because of the importance of the vagus nerve to the digestive tract, you will find much more information about vagal tone in the section 'Combining physical and mental health sciences'.

Sing the stress away!

We already discussed the importance of breathing exercises, as well as meditation and mindfulness. Another beneficial technique is singing, humming, and chanting. This might not be the most intuitive practice, but given that the vagus nerve is connected to the vocal cords and the muscles at the back of the throat, it works. Singing has been shown to increase

HRV and vagal tone. So, if you needed an official excuse to belt out a tune in your car or under the shower, here it is! Thanks to modern science we can now validate the benefits of many ancient spiritual practices, and chanting is certainly one of them. Just think of the chanting of Buddhist monks, the Sanskrit chants of the yogis, the singing of hymns in Christianity, or reciting the Quran in Islam. Native practices all over the world also include singing and chanting for all kinds of rituals.

Freeze the stress away!

If you have been active on social media in 2020 (yes, covid times), you might have heard of the Wim Hof method, which gained a huge interest and following during the pandemic. It's a scientifically validated method including breathwork and cold-water exposure that promises to improve mental health, alongside a few other great benefits regarding physical health and immune function.

Cold water therapy has been successfully used by athletes for faster recovery, decreased delayed onset muscle soreness (DOMS), and increased performance. However, it has now been found that repeated cold-water exposure reduces the adrenaline-driven sympathetic response and increases the parasympathetic activity and calm response. It is, therefore, stipulated that learning how to suppress our natural stress response to cold water will enable us to do so in other unrelated stressful situations and increase our overall resilience. In addition, cold water therapy also seems to have an immediate de-stressing effect, by temporarily impairing cognitive function and inducing a meditative state. This is followed by increased metabolic activity, due to stimulation of the receptors in the skin, and leads to enhanced oxygenation of the blood, heightening alertness and providing greater focus and concentration.

Cold showers can easily be practiced at home. If you want to take it a step further, I recommend having your first cold-water immersion under the guidance of a professional coach or facilitator.

Distress and eustress

Whenever I hold a workshop or seminar that includes a section on stress, which most of my talks do, there is always at least one person who claims to like stress and to be more productive when under stress. As soon as this is mentioned, there will be some agreeing head nods in the audience. I personally also understand and undersign these statements. As a self-proclaimed recovering workaholic, I am still drawn to the rush of adrenaline that comes with seemingly impossible tasks that I then manage to get done, followed by the celebration of achievement – my dopamine levels through the roof.

There are, in fact, two types of stress we can differentiate between – eustress and distress. Eustress feels challenging but manageable, and ultimately leads to growth and success. It literally means 'good stress', consisting of the Greek prefix 'eu', meaning 'good'. Distress, on the contrary, is more difficult and feels daunting and unmanageable.

Not all psychologists and experts agree with this terminology anymore. A recent article criticizes that these labels imply that there is good and bad stress, when in fact there are a wide variety of factors that determine if a person has a positive or negative experience with a certain stressor.[*]

Any given situation might be experienced as rewarding by one person but highly stressful by another. It has been found that the availability of resources determines whether a person can manage the present stress level. We experience eustress when we feel confident and well equipped to deal with a situation or problem. For example, an aspiring marathon runner might be nervous prior to their first race. However, if they know that they have had sufficient training and are well rested and prepared, they know they should be able to do it. Afterward, they will feel a great sense of pride and accomplishment. On the contrary, if we force someone to participate in a marathon who has not partaken in an appropriate training protocol and does not run regularly, they will most probably experience great distress and anxiety.

With that being said, distress doesn't have to be inherently damaging. It might ignite motivation and lead to a better future outcome in some individuals if they are able to rationally acknowledge that they were not prepared for the situation and must establish the resources for the next time a similar event might occur. We can assume that our level of

---

[*]   Bienertova-Vasku J, Lenart P, Scheringer M. Eustress and Distress: Neither Good Nor Bad, but Rather the Same? Bioessays. 2020 Jul;42(7):e1900238. doi: 10.1002/bies.201900238. Epub 2020 Apr 17. PMID: 32302008.

resilience determines how we cope and bounce back from setbacks and distressing events. True resilience, however, is not the ability to remain happy, content, or positive in stressful situations, rather, our ability to be comfortable with uncomfortable situations and feelings and to utilize the challenge for learning and growth.

Experiences that might be perceived as eustress include:

- exercise that is challenging but ultimately suitable to a person's fitness level
- travel that is exhausting, but ultimately rewarding or even relaxing
- work projects that are challenging but achievable
- major life changes, such as moving to different countries or getting married.

Experiences that may trigger distress can include:

- bullying
- manipulative or controlling behavior
- death or severe illness of a loved one
- traumatic events.

The resources that are required to perceive an event as less stressful can be of physical nature – such as money, transport, or a safe home/shelter – or of nonphysical nature – time, knowledge, energy/mental capacity, health/physical ability, steady employment, coping skills, or social support. Stevan Hobfoll's 'Conservation of Resources' theory predicts that individuals with more resources can cope more effectively with adverse events. This theory was successfully put to test in a recent study during COVID-19 lockdowns in Spain.[*]

As discussed earlier, whether a person perceives a situation as a source of positive or negative stress depends on a vast variety of factors, most probably not only the availability of resources. However, it is important to keep in mind that even eustress will turn into distress if there are no adequate rest and recovery periods provided over a prolonged time.

Whilst eustress is, by nature, mostly short term and has a clear solution and defined timeline, distress can be short term, but is more often long term with no known end and outcome. A sensation of being stuck, trapped, and powerless can accompany these events.

Keeping the physiological mechanisms and reactions in mind, even eustress cannot go on indefinitely without ultimately leading to a negative impact on our physical and mental health and well-being. Imagine a young, highly motivated employee, starting their first well-paid job. In the beginning, they will rush to complete every task, every project, as quickly as possible. They will drive high on the epinephrine rush they get from 'just' being able to meet deadlines and bathe in the praise and appreciation they get. They will raise their own bar very high and set expectations. Over time, it might become

---

[*]   Merino, M.D., Vallellano, M.D., Oliver, C. and Mateo, I. (2021), What makes one feel eustress or distress in quarantine? An analysis from conservation of resources (COR) theory. Br J Health Psychol, 26: 606-623. https://doi.org/10.1111/bjhp.12501

challenging to keep up the pace, especially if other factors are thrown into the mix, maybe a life partner, children, or the care of elderly parents. Whatever it is, the once eustress-inducing situation, overtime, becomes toxic and distressing. Resilience declines, and soon, everything feels like too much. Our once bouncy, motivated employee feels overwhelmed and burned out. Even small amounts of stress will now be perceived as distress and might even cause an amygdala hijack. Sounds familiar?

It is our responsibility to take stock of our stress levels on a regular basis and to manage our energy, stress, and physical and mental rest and recovery wisely. We also need to become more aware and realistic about our actual exposure to stress, as well as our current resilience level.

The best way to do that is to assess our baseline stress level. Generally, if we have low baseline stress, are reasonably calm, relaxed, and feel positive, we can deal with oncoming challenges much better and might be able to maintain our optimistic attitude, even if the current stressor is quite intense. However, if we have a high baseline stress level, even low-stress events can push us over the edge. Just remember the function of the amygdala and how it can, if overactive, easily hijack our prefrontal cortex and rational decision-making abilities.

☞ **Exercise:**

To assess your baseline stress accurately, you need to take all aspects of physical and mental stress into consideration. Answer the following questions with 'yes' or 'no'. If you aren't sure, consider the average.

- Does my nutrition promote physical well-being (i.e. do I eat nutritious food in adequate quantities, and do I eat regularly?)
- Does my lifestyle promote physical well-being (i.e. do I move, sleep and rest enough?)
- Does my exercise routine promote physical well-being (i.e. do I engage in exercises that provide a good balance between high-intensity and low-intensity stress on the nervous system and overall body?)
- Does my social life promote mental well-being (i.e. do I have hobbies, engage in mindful and enriching social activities, exchange and communicate openly with friends/family?)
- Does my work life promote mental well-being (i.e. do I feel equipped with the necessary knowledge to handle my job well? Do I feel satisfied at work and can get my work done in a reasonable time? Do I leave work on time?)
- Do my past experiences and mindset promote well-being (i.e. have I found closure with past

experiences? Do I maintain a positive mindset, am I clear about my goals and dreams, and do I feel excited about my life and my future?)

If you answered 0–1 of the above with 'NO', your baseline stress is low. Answering 'NO' to 2–3 is medium and 4 or more would be considered a high baseline stress.

I know many of you reading this might find this rating quite strict, but once we understand the many ways stress interferes with our system and impacts the functioning of all components, we can no longer ignore the tremendous effect of stress on our whole being. Chronic stress, of any kind, triggers oxidative stress, during which free radicals damage our cell DNA and can cause tissue degeneration, increase the risks of disease, and accelerate the aging process.

Are you addicted to stress?

There is no arguing that the stress response of the sympathetic nervous system can give us advantages and even feel good at times. Our muscles are pumping, heart and breath rates are elevated, our bloodstream is full of energy, and we feel high on the rush of hormones our adrenal glands are producing. All of this increases our performance, alertness, and makes us feel sharp and productive.

But have you ever struggled to relax and calm back down after a stressful time at work? Did you find yourself secretly missing the tight deadlines, the pressure, and the sleepless nights? Do you actually dislike relaxing and hate doing nothing? You might be a stress junkie! And there is a scientific explanation for this phenomenon.

Alongside the previously mentioned hormonal responses, research has found that cortisol can make a region in the brain called the nucleus accumbens more sensitive to dopamine. You might have heard about dopamine as one of the 'feel good' hormones. Dopamine is, in fact, a neurotransmitter that is involved in many neurological and physiological functions. It plays a contributing factor in correct motor function, mood, decision making, and is associated with movement disorders such as Parkinson's disease and psychiatric disorders such as attention deficit disorders. Dopamine is made in the brain, in the substantia nigra, ventral tegmental area, and the hypothalamus and acts as a chemical messenger between neurons.

Dopamine is released when your brain is expecting a reward such as food, shopping, sex, or anything else you enjoy. The anticipation alone may be enough to raise dopamine levels once we associate a certain activity with pleasure. If, for example, your favorite treat is homemade chocolate cake, your brain might increase dopamine when you smell the cake baking or you see it being cut in front of you. Even if somebody mentions baking chocolate cake, a little dopamine may be released. When you finally eat it, the high level of dopamine will reinforce this craving and make you want to satisfy it again in the future. It is a powerful cycle of motivation, reward, and reinforcement and plays an important role in many cravings and addictions. Many smokers, for example, consider a cigarette break a reward for work, or they may link smoking to other pleasurable events. This makes quitting much harder than the actual nicotine withdrawal. If our expectations get disappointed, our dopamine levels get lowered and that will in turn affect our mood, as well as increase the cravings.

Of course, there is a lot more to dopamine and its many functions are just one component of other sensitive neurological circuits. For example, dopamine systems contribute to the generation of the stress response, as well as to our stress coping mechanisms. The earlier mentioned fact that dopamine levels increase not only as a response to pleasure but also to stress is a recent finding that changes our understanding of stress addiction.

There are different theories about the importance of dopamine in motivation and if some individuals might have higher dopamine levels or are more driven and affected by dopamine than others. The new field of neuroeconomics, which combines psychology, economics, and neuroscience, has investigated go-getters and Type A personalities. It has been found that individuals with high levels of dopamine are more likely to work harder to achieve goals as well as experience larger reward sensations; those with low levels of dopamine preferred the easier route and got smaller reward feelings. This is a new area of research and needs more validation. Regardless, whether it is true or not, it is important to recognize our own stress dependencies.

If you consider yourself a Type A personality, which is associated with high achievement, competitiveness, high motivation, and impatience, then your natural inclination to embrace and thrive in fast-paced environments can lead to unchecked cortisol levels. If you find yourself in a work environment marked by the constant need to achieve and deliver under stressful conditions, your chronically stressed brain might become dependent on the euphoric release of dopamine. In this case, you would have turned into a stress junkie!

We know that stress can cause a 'natural high' by activating the arousal and attention centers in the peripheral nervous system, but it can also wake the neural circuitry underlying desire and cravings. Just like that, stress has become your new homemade chocolate cake.

Another reason why many people seem to embrace stress, and even actively add to their already-stressful schedules, is that obsessing over work allows us to avoid self-reflection and having to acknowledge our own unhappiness. In a later chapter, we will look more into the different ways we need to introduce excitement and euphoria back into our lives to avoid stress dependency.

Breaking the stress cycle

If you have now identified that you have far too much stress in your life, or maybe even have concluded that you are addicted to stress, then you can begin your conscious recovery progress. A little forewarning: understand that relaxation can feel challenging and even uncomfortable at first – physically and mentally. Coming off the cascade of stress hormones that your brain has become accustomed to might leave you feeling weak, lethargic, and lazy. You might experience mental withdrawal symptoms as your brain craves its usual rush of cortisol and dopamine. Physically, your body will also be crashing from the elevated state of performance that it has been in for a prolonged period.

Did it ever happen to you that you made it through a highly stressful work project just to fall sick on your first day of vacation? This is quite a common phenomenon and a result of our weakened immune system. The reason we only get that nasty cold when we have some rest is simply because that's when our body can finally let go, no longer needing to run in overdrive.

I realize that I'm not making destressing sound appealing, but just remember that chronic stress will most definitely have severe long-term effects on your physical and mental health.

Baby steps for stress recovery

To make the recovery process smooth and enjoyable, it is important to take baby steps and not go cold turkey. As you can tell, you might want to take stress addiction as seriously as any other addiction. If you think about it, stress has a similarly tremendous, negative impact on your social life, relationships, health, and mindset, as with other addictions. It is just as controlling and will have a great effect on how you live your life. The same applies even if you don't think you're addicted but are simply exposed to chronic stress.

Take baby steps and get yourself used to the sensation of relaxation again. Engage in activities that you find destressing and relaxing for short periods of time. This can be anything from breathing (yes, breathing always works!), to listening to music, going for a relaxed walk, and journaling to simply doing nothing for a few minutes. When you begin, pay close attention to your resistance level. If you start to feel restless, your mind starts to go back to work, you begin to engage with worrisome thoughts, or you start to engage in other activities such as checking your emails, then either shorten the duration of your practice or try something else. These short relaxation periods must feel enjoyable, not like a chore. You will benefit more from frequent, short sessions than infrequent long sessions. Once your resistance decreases, you can lengthen the time. This will help your brain get used to the relaxation response as well as to switching between parasympathetic and sympathetic nervous system activation.

What are anti-stress hormones?

You have now read a lot about stress responses, stress-regulating hormones, neurotransmitters, and circuitries. It might be feeling a bit heavy at the moment. But, there is good news. Fortunately, our brains also produces stress-busting chemicals that we can use to our advantage.

Oxytocin, for example, is a hormone that is produced in the hypothalamus and released by the pituitary gland into the bloodstream. You might have heard of oxytocin as the love hormone, as it plays a crucial role in childbirth as well as bonding and falling in love. However, this powerful happy hormone has many more crucial functions; it can induce anti-stress effects such as the reduction of cortisol levels and blood pressure, the increase in our pain threshold, decreased sensations of fear and anxiety, the promotion of positive social interactions, and overall healthy growth and healing.

It was previously assumed that, aside from an autonomic release during childbirth, oxytocin would only be released through touch and positive social interactions related to love. But it has now been found that there are more ways to benefit from it. Ingestion of food triggers a release through an activation of vagal nerve afferents (remember the importance of the vagal nerve when it comes to digestion). The stimulation of other senses such as olfaction seems to increase oxytocin, as well as sound and light. In addition, purely psychological mechanisms such as feelings and thoughts of gratitude, love, and compassion help to elevate our oxytocin levels. (Remember that mind-body connection thing we've been talking about?)

Another chemical that has recently gained popularity in neuroscientific research and psychology is gamma aminobutyric acid (GABA). This non-protein amino acid neurotransmitter is the most common inhibitory neurotransmitter in our central nervous system. This means that it prevents or blocks chemical messaging and decreases nerve cell stimulation in the brain. GABA is known for producing a calming effect and is said to have a major role in controlling hyperactivity associated with stress, fear, and anxiety. GABA binds to specific receptors on nerve cells (GABA-A and GABA-B receptors) and decreases their responsiveness, lessening the cells' ability to receive and send chemical messages to other cells. By slowing certain brain functions triggered during the fight-or-flight response, GABA may be able to reduce stress and anxiety and improve sleep quality. GABA appears to modulate our brainwaves and promote balance between the alpha and beta brainwaves. Alpha brainwaves help to calm and relax the body and are the connection between the subconscious and the conscious mind. Beta waves, on the other hand, are involved in logical thinking and our conscious thought – they have a stimulating effect.

Low GABA levels have been linked to mental health issues such as anxiety, panic attacks, insomnia, and obsessive-compulsive disorders, as well as convulsions. GABA is a key chemical in the stimulation and secretion of pancreatic enzymes and low levels can lead to bloating, malabsorption, and flatulence.

Our body naturally produces GABA via a complex chemical process from the amino acid L-glutamine. Vitamin B6, Zinc, and L-taurine play a supporting role in converting Glutamine into GABA. Glutamine is first converted into glutamate, the most abundant excitatory neurotransmitter, responsible for memory function, learning ability, attention span, and the metabolism of carbohydrates. An enzyme (glutamate decarboxylase) then converts glutamate into GABA with the help of Vitamin B6. Low levels of B6 can lead to low productivity of this enzyme and are often observed with health conditions, including heart diseases and Alzheimer's.

L-taurine, an amino acid, also aids the communication and productivity of glutamate decarboxylase, and animal studies have verified a link between anxiety and taurine deficiency. Zinc promotes the release of GABA from the receptors. Like

Vitamin B6, Zinc is essential for important brain chemicals, including dopamine, adrenaline and noradrenaline, histamine, and serotonin. Serotonin, another inhibitory neurotransmitter, enhances and improves the effects of GABA.

As you can tell, GABA might play quite an important role in our mental well-being and happiness. It has become widely available as a supplement, and many people report a beneficial effect on sleep, mood, and a sensation of calmness. Scientifically, however, it still isn't clear how well GABA is absorbed, if it's absorbed at all, when taken orally.* It was initially believed that GABA couldn't cross the blood-brain barrier, but more recent studies claim it might be able. A 2016 article showed a significant improvement in sleep after oral consumption of GABA supplements.

Research does, however, agree that exercise seems to be a certain way to increase not only GABA but also glutamate levels. Yoga, as well as cardiovascular exercise with varying intensities, have been found to promote our well-being and mood.

Is stress physical or mental?

The more we discover about the physiological and psychological mechanisms of stress, and its appearance and effects, the more questions arise. Relatively new areas

---

* Yamatsu A, Yamashita Y, Pandharipande T, Maru I, Kim M. Effect of oral γ-aminobutyric acid (GABA) administration on sleep and its absorption in humans. Food Sci Biotechnol. 2016 Apr 30;25(2):547-551. doi: 10.1007/s10068-016-0076-9. PMID: 30263304; PMCID: PMC6049207.

of science, such as Neuroeconomics, Neurophysiology, and Neuropsychology are aiming to uncover and explain the many ways our mind, nervous system, and physical body are interconnected and are controlling our behavior, health, and each other. Stress, just like any other chemical reaction in the brain and body, is complex. However, as I've said before, this complexity serves to further equip us with a wide variety of opportunities for prevention and treatment, even without being a specialist. Let us not forget, we are talking about YOUR body, YOUR mind, YOUR health and happiness, not just theoretical models.

Even as I'm writing this chapter, I'm once again amazed by the many details we must understand to promote our own health and well-being. It might not seem like it, but I have tried to keep it short and to focus on the minimum that I believe to be important. However, I am not expecting everyone to enjoy the little details as much as I am, so let me try to summarize!

Scientific evidence shows that anxiety disorders and chronic stress are a result of dysfunctional modulation of the brain circuits that regulate emotional responses to potentially dangerous situations. This understanding of mental disorders as a disturbance of emotional response regulation allows for anxiety and stress disorders to be assessed and treated from psychological, behavioral, as well as pharmacological avenues.

Stress responses in the brain involve bottom-up activity from the amygdala and top-down control mechanisms from the prefrontal cortex. Understanding the different ways (psychological and neurological) these mechanisms might be disabled or disturbed, gives us ways to identify the most effective strategies to rebalance our stress responses and restore chemical balance in the brain.

✳ Key points:

✳ What is stress: When the brain perceives something as threatening, it triggers the release of cortisol, epinephrine (adrenaline), and other stress hormones to help the body through the experience of the present stressor.

✳ The negative effects of stress: Stress, in and of itself, is natural and designed to help us out of life-threatening situations, but long-term and/or frequent exposure to stress can negatively affect our health as our bodies are unable to properly switch into a resting state in order to process, digest, and regulate.

✳ How to recognize the stress responses and help ourselves out of it: Once we know more about how the brain works and how our body can influence the mind, we can exercise a plethora of techniques to help bring ourselves out of that heightened state of stress and back into a place of controlled, rational thought.

✳ Stress addiction: The rush of adrenaline and the euphoria that can follow a stressful situation may sometimes incentivize us to seek stress out, feeling uncomfortable when we're made to sit still and focus on rest. This is stress addiction – it is a real thing.

✳ The neurotransmitter ecosystem: Our bodies naturally produce stress hormones as well as hormones that help reduce stress; it's a relationship between hormones and neurotransmitters. As we learn more about how this works, we can actively play our part in this relationship.

Childhood and Adult Trauma

If you follow social media accounts, read publications, or listen to podcasts of coaches and psychologists these days, you might easily conclude that everybody has experienced childhood trauma. Indeed, one could argue that many of us, if not most, have been exposed to an upbringing that was not ideal, and maybe created some sort of emotional withdrawal, stonewalling, anger or resentment issues, or decreased self-esteem and self-value. The concepts of conscious parenting and emotional intelligence have only recently become popular and, therefore, you might have been brought up by parents that were still unconsciously dealing with their own childhood trauma.

Living and working in an extremely multicultural environment (the United Arab Emirates) has opened my eyes to a simple fact: regardless of our cultural, religious, social-economic, or educational background, most of us have been raised by parents who were operating on very different parenting schemes and ideologies. They probably did their best and loved you dearly but were, to some extent, not equipped to prepare you emotionally for the life you were going to lead. As a matter of fact, as parents, we can really only act based on our own experiences. Our world is changing so quickly, however, that even the most conscious parents cannot know what characteristics, attitudes, and strengths their children will require in order to succeed in adulthood. All we can do is raise our children to be confident, self-aware, and resilient.

Because of the generational differences and the parenting styles your own parents were exposed to, you might have had to take on the role of a caretaker, 'good child', a supporter of siblings or parents, scapegoat, emotional garbage bin, punching bag, or other sub-ideal role to better cope during your childhood. These positions can all be difficult to handle as a child and hinder your own emotional development, practice of coping strategies, and self-care.

Most of my clients had at least one emotionally unavailable parent. People that are emotionally unavailable are uncomfortable and awkward with emotions, especially the 'big emotions' that children have. They might not be able to listen or may feel the need to invalidate you and your feelings. They might not be great at expressing their love or celebrating your accomplishments. They might also not often ask about you or your life, or they may just stick to more superficial topics. These parents can be very supportive in other ways, for example, with financial support, attending sporting events, etc., but might not be able to connect in other meaningful ways conducive to relationship growth. Children of emotionally unavailable parents often don't feel 'heard', 'seen', or 'understood'. The parent might feel more like a familiar stranger. Sometimes this leads children to act up, as they try to get the attention they crave. It's also not unusual for children to exaggerate, or even invent dramatic stories. Having been raised by emotionally unavailable parents might lead to anger and resentment toward the parents, but most importantly, it often leads to beliefs such as:

'My feelings don't matter.'

'I cannot ask for help.'

'I have to do everything by myself.'

'No one cares about me and my struggles.'

There's often a feeling of emptiness that we try to fill, with food, relationships, impulsive spending, gambling, or something else that numbs the void.

I am describing this phenomenon because it is common. If you think that it's the case for you, try to understand your parents' upbringing and you will likely find an explanation for them needing to protect themselves emotionally. Whatever parenting style we were exposed to, it is important to recognize our parents' limitations and the fact that they were acting based on their own upbringing, the situation and environment they were in. Most importantly, they were raising you to their best abilities. You might have heard the term, 'breaking the cycle'; I believe parenting is the most important, most sacred, area in which we can make a difference and create more wealthy, healthy, and connected societies. Whether you have or want to have children, or not, we all need to be part of an emotionally aware society to create change moving forward.

Fortunately, we are moving in the right direction, and the definition and parameters of childhood trauma have changed greatly. They now include many emotional factors that would have previously not been taken into consideration. The National Institute of Mental Health describes childhood trauma as:

'A child's experience of an event that is emotionally painful or distressful, which often results in lasting mental and physical effects.'

It is important to note that we are no longer talking about one-off traumatic events (only), but rather the subjective experience of an event. Hence, we acknowledge that if the same situation happens to different people, some cases can result in 'childhood trauma' whilst others can display more resilience based on the subjective emotional outcome. It is, therefore, solely up to you to define if you have, indeed, experienced any sort of trauma. The above definition can be helpful to assess if any events, or ongoing situations, have resulted in any mental or physical impact that might still be affecting your emotional experience and way of thinking.

Because of our individual perceptions, there are many people with the experience and memory of happy childhoods, which satisfied all their emotional needs and enriched and enabled their growth and spiritual development – childhoods that were full of love, compassion, and care from their parents and surroundings. But there are also many people who couldn't develop their emotional intelligence fully and need to catch up in adulthood to lead better, happier lives.

Childhood Trauma vs Adult Trauma

Childhood Trauma has become, as I mentioned earlier, a popular topic. 'Inner child healing' and trauma-informed' sessions have found their way into yoga studios, sound healing sessions, coaching, and counseling. So then, you might wonder, what is Adult Trauma? Does it even exist? And why do we hear so much more about childhood trauma? Let's begin by establishing that trauma in adulthood certainly does exist.

A definition by the American Psychological Association (APA) defines trauma as:

'An emotional response to a terrible event like an accident, rape, or natural disaster.'

Here we have a definition that, whilst still highlighting the subjective emotional response, also adds the factor of a traumatic event. The events listed in the definition are horrible situations that might well result in post-traumatic stress disorder (PTSD). However, I believe that there is an urgent need to discuss and validate other types of adult trauma, which, in my opinion, should have a similar definition to the childhood trauma above and be more inclusive and highlight the importance of our personal perception of an event.

The reason that the focus of modern psychology has been on childhood trauma is the understanding that the young brain is notably more susceptive to influences and experiences (see 'Our thoughts create our reality' and

'Master your paradigm shift'). The brain is constantly taking in and processing new information. Neuroscience teaches us that every thought, every concept, every idea, every stimulus results in physiological changes to the brain. As you are reading this, your brain is changing. New information sparks new neurological pathways, connecting these pieces of information to existing, stored thoughts. The younger the brain, the less old information exists. Therefore, every experience is thought to have greater impact and power on the moldable young mind, resulting in long-lasting emotional changes.

The impact of trauma on the child's brain, or rather the imprint on the brain's neurobiological wiring and resulting altered brain activity, might be more significant when compared to the adult's brain because of the function of the prefrontal cortex. This part of the brain plays a vital role in controlling cognitive functions, including impulse control and moderating social behavior. The prefrontal cortex is the last part of the brain to develop, beginning throughout adolescence and reaching full maturity by the age of 25. Prior to that, humans are practicing emotion regulation and decision making based on more rudimental and primal parts of the brain, which are greatly ruled by our survival instinct and need for safety (read more in 'What is Stress').

We know, however, that our brains are still constantly changing as we get older. So, what about repetitive exposure to emotionally painful or distressful events as an adult? Whilst we know that childhood exposure might probably result in quicker, maybe more severe, brain alterations, these events can certainly still change an adult's brain as well as their behavior and emotional response to events. Every experience that we have throughout our lives impacts the way we think, feel, and act. Of course, the adverse events we might have experienced in childhood and our resulting level of emotional awareness and development are crucial factors in our response and perception of situations we are exposed to in adulthood.

I like to imagine our brain as a landscape with many rivers, lakes, streams, and creeks. The first stimulus to ever arrive in your brain started a tiny, thin creek. With repetitive confirmation of this information, it eventually turned into a river, maybe even a strong waterfall. Let's take parental love for example. The immature infant brain needs the sensation of love and bonding to thrive. We know that babies who are being fed and watered but not held nor talked to are not capable of survival. The primal part of the brain, the brain stem, needs to feel physically and emotionally safe. Without this safety (or loving action), nature assumes that the infant would not be sufficiently supported and equipped to survive. More importantly, however, the brain stem gets stressed and switches into survival mode, which inhibits brain development. This lack of brain stimulation results in death. The effects of stress on brain function are mentioned in several chapters of this book.

Now, back to our little stream of love, comfort, and safety that has begun to form in our brain landscape. Let us assume that there is more water (love) running down the stream, and over time the riverbed deepens and the stream turns into a nice, strong river. Let us now suppose that, from early on, our young child has learned that there are conditions attached to love. Maybe being 'good' was something stressed upon by the caretakers. This, by the way, can be fully accidental and something as innocent as a choice of words and situations. 'You've been such a good boy/girl. I love you!' Without saying 'I love you' often and randomly, the child may begin to draw certain conclusions. Remember we are still talking about a very young brain without much experience and without the ability to rationalize or compartmentalize. The concept of being good and receiving love can become firmly intertwined. The two become one in our strong river of love. This is how we all build and create our understanding of the world, with every single aspect of our experiences. Furthermore, we will store information and concepts that we perceive to be true ('I need to be good to be loved – I need to deserve love') in our subconscious mind. In this way, new experiences don't need to be extensively analyzed. Rather, they're immediately sent down the same river as all the other similar experiences before. Our brain likes to be efficient and not waste time on what it has already considered true before. We compartmentalize information!

Let us fast forward two decades. Our young adult is now starting to experience love and the expression of love through potential partners. Maybe a wonderful person offers unconditional love. Because this is an unusual and new concept, it might be like a drop in the ocean and go unnoticed, that is, unless it is repeatedly experienced. The previously learned beliefs are stronger than the reality currently being experienced. The good news is that this doesn't mean we can't change the way we perceive the world and our reality; we will discuss this later (see the chapter on paradigms).

This is not an example of childhood trauma but a quick hypothetical example of how the brain, our emotional experience, and our beliefs are formed and developed in childhood. However, the same principles can be applied to experiences that happen later in life. The difference is that a little more time and repetition is needed to create their own river, or they might simply attach themselves to existing rivers.

Let's continue our situation of adult trauma based on the previously mentioned understanding of love ('I need to deserve love'). Without going into too much detail, imagine a situation whereby our young adult person finds themselves in an abusive relationship with a controlling partner. Due to the repetitive abuse, the belief 'I need to deserve love' might turn into 'I don't deserve love'. This would open the door to even more abuse and a lack, or absence, of any self-value and self-love and result in a downward spiral.

From my experience, adult trauma and its effect can sometimes be difficult to recognize by the victim themself, simply because the intrinsic enabling factors (our inner understanding of the situation) are perceived as the absolute truth. Our thoughts and emotions create our reality, and it is often easier to blame ourselves for situations and to suffer than to acknowledge that there might be a different reality, different opportunities, and different potential outcomes. Every person has a different understanding and response to a given situation, even our loved ones and friends. But stepping out of our victim mentality would require us, once again, to take responsibility and ownership. If you read the chapter 'The Knowledge Gap', you might be noticing a bit of a recurring theme here.

Once concepts are deeply anchored in the subconscious mind, a lot of conscious uncoupling of different thoughts has to happen if we want to change. In our mind, we have created a construct of many ideas and events and have connected them to one undeniable truth; we are no longer looking at the individual thought and event as separate units – we have completely intertwined them. Our emotional reaction to this truth happens subconsciously and is an automated response. In the beginning of the uncoupling progress, it might take weeks or even months until we realize our automated response mechanisms, but with a little practice, it gets much easier and faster (see 'How to create your paradigm shift').

Of course, we can experience adult trauma that is completely detached from any existing memories or previous experiences. One of my clients had a wonderful childhood in a safe environment. She clearly remembers long summers with her parents and two siblings. The dog, the picket fence, the many friends in school – everything was perfect. She remembers spending weekends doing charitable work with her dad and gardening with mum. The parents are still very much in love, and she has a great relationship with both siblings. She always had good grades in school and enjoyed learning. Early on, she knew what kind of career she wanted to pursue, and after some traveling after university, she successfully completed an internship that she enjoyed and gained much experience in.

Then she landed her first proper job. She still remembers the excitement and confidence she felt on her first day at work. But very quickly, events turned sour as she started to be the victim of bullying by a co-worker. This had never happened to her before; she had always been popular and liked by everyone. At first, she was determined not to let it affect her. However, after two years, she decided to no longer expose herself to the daily stress she experienced and moved on to another job.

This time the first day was overshadowed by anxiety. Whilst she wasn't bullied during this second work employment, she strongly felt held back by a superior, as if she wasn't given the opportunity to grow. Her story continued in a similar manner until I met her about five years after she started that second work engagement. By then she was insecure about her professional abilities, had no confidence in the workplace, and, on top of that, was in a personal relationship in which her intelligence and abilities were constantly undermined and belittled. The small stream of bullying had turned into a destructive waterfall of 'I am not smart enough' and 'I can't do this'.

The reasons or ways she was bullied in her first job are irrelevant, simply because other people's actions and opinions really do not matter. What matters is our perception and our emotional response to it. Everyone we interact with, including the people we intimately know ('in and out' as we like to say), has a completely different brain landscape than us. Because of this, we all have different communication styles; different understanding of concepts, thoughts, and ideas; and different ways of thinking. However, when we allow ourselves to connect to thoughts and beliefs, we must become aware of their power and the fact that they might likely be able to influence, or even control, our emotional experiences in a wide variety of situations.

☞ **Exercise:**

Find an object with a distinct color and ask three people what their immediate association with this color is. Obviously, you pick your own association as well. Then exchange what that color means to you and what it brings up. I am guessing there were many different answers.

Now imagine what happens when you describe emotions, feelings, situations, and events to other people and how completely different their association and interpretation will be!

As you are reading this, you might have many new thoughts being sparked. You might find yourself accepting the concepts I am presenting, or you might find yourself rejecting these ideas. Whichever it is, take a moment to think about which concepts, understandings, and realities you have about these topics and what your truth is. Maybe discuss it with someone else and get an understanding of how they see the world.

I mentioned before that we compartmentalize thoughts and that our brain will try to connect new information to old, previously acquired knowledge. Therefore, our brains are not comfortable with change, and change is challenging. Our bodies and minds resist alterations simply because they are perceived unsafe.

The fear of the unknown is greater than the known fear!

There is great safety in what we know, even if the known is filled with unhappiness, stress, despair, and fear. The gift of humanity is comprehension, understanding, awareness, and the ability to analyze situations and events. Throughout this book, I invite you to reach a deeper level of consciousness, to gain the ability to analyze your subconscious understanding of the world, and to make conscious choices about your reality.

Reality Testing

Reality testing is a concept initially brought about by Sigmund Freud, used by therapists and coaches to assist clients in distinguishing their internal thoughts, feelings, and ideas from the factual, real events. In other words, it gives us the ability to see a situation for what it really is by helping us differentiate between how an event made us feel and how the event actually played out. It helps us focus on the play-by-play physicality of what took place, rather than what we hope or fear it might mean. The usefulness of reality testing extends beyond a therapeutic setting. The need to appropriately distinguish our inner world from reality is something that's relevant to everyone; it can be a very helpful exercise.

Examples:

Example 1: 'I said good morning to Jane in the hall this morning, but she didn't answer. She must be mad at me for something I have done.'

Reality: There may be many other explanations for this. She didn't see you; she was deep in thought, or she is grumpy today and has a lot on her mind.

Example 2: 'I just failed my first exam of the year. This must mean that I am now bound to fail the rest of my exams as well.'

Reality: Failing at something initially does not equate to a pattern of failure and does not mean that things cannot improve or change in the future.

☞ **Exercise:**

Your turn:

Go through a few scenarios that happened to you recently and describe your emotional reaction; then try to formulate a simple, non-emotional sentence with the actual reality.

✳ **Key points:**

- ✳ What is trauma: Lasting mental and/or physical effects in response to a particular event that has taken place in our lives.
- ✳ Childhood trauma and adult trauma: Given the increased plasticity of a younger brain, children are more likely to take events they're exposed to as foundational pieces of their reality – perceiving their

world through the lens of this experience. Adults are also susceptible to having their perceptions of themselves and the world altered by experiences, but it often takes long-term or intense exposure to a certain event for trauma to take root.

* The brain landscape and our internal reality: Our brains are actively shaping and rewiring based on what connections have proven to serve us most. These areas of repeat use form the construct through which we filter our worlds.

* Reality testing: This is a simple and quick way to help us get around our reality filters. This is a method through which a therapist can help a patient distinguish between their internal perception of a moment and the actual events that took place – but you can also use it for yourself.

III : Combining Physical and Mental Health Sciences

We are intuitively aware of our mind-body connection and would never argue that it doesn't exist. There are many sayings that describe this connection, such as 'butterflies in our stomach', 'gut feeling', 'thinking with the heart', and many more. The link between our minds and bodies holds a wealth of unused potential for prevention, healing, and optimizing our physical and mental experience. Science and medicine have long acknowledged that the way we think, our stress levels, and our lifestyles can negatively impact our health, sometimes with terminal effects. However, cultivating a positive, resilient mindset; active relaxation techniques; and beneficial nutrition/activity habits are not utilized, or even prescribed, to prevent, cure, or reverse these outcomes.

What is less known is that the mind-body connection is so complete that even the way we think affects our physiological body. Every thought we have creates a chemical release, which is called a feeling or an emotion. When we think of a negative thought and feel the associated negative emotions, the body will chemically understand it and be affected by this.

We could say that knowledge is for the mind, but experience is manifested in the body. We begin to embody the repetitive thoughts, the things we tell ourselves about our perceived reality.

Fortunately, if we choose to change our mindset, our thought patterns, and our daily beliefs, we can rewrite these programs and create new neurological signaling that will result in an altered physiological state and recondition our physical capability. The body and the brain are constantly changing, which means that all that stands between you and a different mind and body is your conscious decision to change! As long as you continue to think the same thoughts, your body will store and execute the same programs, resulting in the same outcome.

Remember: **You are the creator of your life!**

If you are ready to facilitate the change, then your job is to put the knowledge you will gain from this next chapter into an experience, to move it from your mind to your body, from thinking to doing and then to being. When you begin to consciously apply these simple principles, you will experience a shift in your energy or frequency.

As mentioned earlier, we think approximately 60 to 70 thousand thoughts every day, and it's estimated that 90% of these thoughts are repetitive. These redundant thoughts produce the same effects on the body, day in and day out. You are feeding your body the identical information and energy, and, therefore, you keep creating the same, repetitive life for yourself. The same thoughts will lead you to make the same choices and the same choices will result in the same behavior and emotional experience. Your neurochemistry, your hormones, even your genetic profile will all align to match these thoughts – over and over again until your body becomes your thoughts.

So how can we break this cycle? If we become aware of our concepts and subconscious habits, then we can create new neurological synapses. We can adjust the way we think, talk, and behave. We can make an active choice to leave old, outdated thoughts and emotions in the past and enable ourselves to create a new mental and physical experience.

On top of these powerful insights about the impact of our mind on the body, we can do even more! You will learn how the physiological body affects your hormones and neurotransmitters, and you will be able to create the physiological foundation for your Happiness Frequency. If used together, this approach fast-tracks your change and primes your whole system to create the best version of yourself, from the inside out.

With all that being said, let's look into a powerful way of facilitating change in our body – our nutrition!

How nutrition affects our mental health

In the previous section, we learned about the many ways our body, brain, mind, behavior, and emotions are closely interdependent and connected. But there is still so much more to discover and so many more ways in which we can actively influence how we feel, enabling our bodies and minds to be balanced and happy. It really is startling that, despite all the scientific evidence and discoveries, we are not yet, by default, using an integrative health and nutrition approach to prevent many lifestyle diseases, mental health problems, and other stress-induced illnesses.

Again, I am certainly not blaming the medical system. I'm simply pushing for a proactive and independent approach to our own health care. It is time that we utilize our constantly increasing knowledge about our wonderful and complex body systems. If, as individuals, we don't have the necessary expertise, it is up to us to find, research, and investigate lifestyle adjustments that suit our needs. You might be surprised to learn that approaching mental health issues with holistic, physiological care is not as complicated as you might have thought. Once we get into the practice of considering the bigger picture, and the effects that any event can have on not just one but several body systems, it quickly becomes a habit.

More importantly, the results can really be mind-blowing and unexpected! In a follow-up session with a previous client, he told me that his life had changed so much since we started working together that he couldn't even remember how he felt before. However, when he shared his story with friends and family members, they couldn't quite appreciate how much his inner experience had changed; to the outside, it just seemed like he'd made some small alterations to his diet and lifestyle. This is true. However, in his case, these outwardly small modifications were all that was required to allow his body and mind to reset, rebalance and enable him to be much happier in body and mind. Every story is different, of course. For some people, it is a small mindset shift. For others, a drastic diet change. For another person, it might be integrating breathing exercises. Whatever it is that sets off the desired difference will normally create a ripple effect and result in a variety of noticeable, positive outcomes.

Sometimes it helps to begin an intervention with a different approach, however, and to really look at the bigger picture. I have just recently worked with a client who experienced severe symptoms of depression. This was not the first time this person had been through a rough time, and the debilitating feelings and the huge impact on their life were all too familiar. My client had taken short courses of anti-depressants in the past, and we had successfully used that time to reset their mental state, mindset, and mood; together with the psychiatrist, we aimed to get them off the meds as soon as possible. As we were discussing the best possible procedure in this last instance, however, something did not sum up for me. The onset of the depression was a bit sudden, and somehow, to me, it felt different from the previous episodes. I suggested seeing an internal medicine specialist who I knew to be quite thorough. Long story short, my client had severe B-Vitamin deficiency, as well as anemia. After three months of Vitamin B12 IV's and supplementation, they felt perfectly happy and balanced. The deficiencies were most probably caused by a prolonged course of antibiotics for an unrelated health concern but could not be 100% confirmed. Of course, we still complimented the treatment with coaching sessions to establish a strong mindset and help to promote psychological well-being, even though the depression was a result of a physiological cause.

This is just one of many examples that I can recall when a physical imbalance created mental health issues in a client. Of course, depression that develops through adverse experiences and trauma will ultimately also result in a physiological imbalance and greatly impact our health. There might be many instances when the two go together to promote our unwellness.

However, in my daily work with clients, I no longer spend too much time investigating the 'why'. In my opinion, defining the chicken and egg does not necessarily lead us to find better solutions, unless in a more uncommon example as mentioned above. Of course, it is tempting to try to understand why we are suddenly experiencing all these feelings of low mood, anxiety, and depression. Parents are often especially concerned about finding all the answers for their children and teens when they are having a rough time – understandably so. But even if we were fully aware of the exact cause(s), that does not mean we can fully prevent it from happening again. A much more impactful prevention is to align our lifestyles as much as possible to promote physical and mental happiness and balance. This supports a more positive mindset, even when life throws hardship, sorrow, and traumatic events at us. Rather than wasting time wondering how we got to a place of unwellness, we need to take responsibility in actively creating our future and carefully curate our goals, dreams, and the path to reach them. The purpose of our human existence is to live our best lives. It is our duty to create internal happiness and balance and to be prepared for external negativity, which unfortunately we cannot always prevent.

Changing the body

As with our brain, the body is also constantly changing. Every day, 330 billion cells are replaced, which is the equivalent of about one percent of all cells. In 100 days, about 30 trillion cells have been renewed, which is the equivalent of a whole new you. Of course, this is not to be taken literally, as some cells, like most of the skin and gut, are replaced within a few months, whereas others take years or might even stay with us forever.

Nevertheless, everything we intake, our dietary habits, as well as anything we 'consume' with our brain is the building material for new neurological pathways, new physiological cells and, therefore, our future self! Isn't that so cool? This is a fact that I find absolutely mind-blowing. Every decision, every thought, every bit of food, every drink, every action has a purpose, an impact, and, with that, great importance. You might find this idea daunting, but it is also hugely empowering.

In recent years, there have been interesting studies demonstrating the benefits and effects of nutrition on our mental health. Following two earthquakes in New Zealand in 2010 and 2011, research participants were given high doses of micronutrients and reported significantly lower levels of depression, post-traumatic stress, and anxiety compared to a test group. These results were also verified by other studies.[*][†]

Whilst science is catching up with this long-overseen, cost-effective, and easy treatment method for mental health[‡], both in terms of prevention and treatment, we can already use existing knowledge to our advantage. There are many ways in which our nutrition affects our mental health. I will try to keep it structured into three main areas: our energy levels, our gut bacteria, and our endocrine system. However, you will see that it is impossible to clearly separate the effects. Of course, as is the case with everything in this book, they are tightly intertwined. Remember, this book aims to empower you to make better choices, but the ones most impactful are probably the ones you are not going to find most intuitive, or easy. If you consider your diet and nutritional habits to be quite good, even after reading this chapter, then I recommend focusing your energy on making changes in other areas. Don't overwhelm yourself.

---

[*]   Rucklidge, J. J., Andridge, R., Gorman, B., Blampied, N., Gordon, H., & Boggis, A. (2012). Shaken but unstirred? Effects of micronutrients on stress and trauma after an earthquake: RCT evidence comparing formulas and doses. *Human Psychopharmacology: Clinical and Experimental, 27*, 440-454.

[†]   Rucklidge, J. J., & Blampied, N. M. (2011). Post-earthquake psychological functioning in adults with attention-deficit/hyperactivity disorder: Positive effects of micronutrients on resilience. *New Zealand Journal of Psychology, 40*, 51-57.

[‡]   Jacka, F. N., O'Neil, A., Opie, R., Itsiopoulos, C., Cotton, S., Mohebbi, M., ... & Brazionis, L. (2017). A randomised controlled trial of dietary improvement for adults with major depression (the 'SMILES' trial). *BMC Medicine, 15*, 23.

Again, things are likely going to fall in place once you start the process. However, going from pretty-good nutrition to perfect nutrition will only result in minor improvements.

Nutrition 101

We all know that food provides the energy for us to be active as well as the fuel and building material for many physiological processes. However, we tend to be quite unintentional with how we nurture and treat our bodies and don't necessarily match our nutritional needs with what we provide. Hence there is the potential that many of our requirements will not be met as we proceed to overload our system with unnecessary ingredients.

Let's dive into a quick crash course in nutrition science!

Some definitions to start:

Nutrient: A chemical compound (e.g. carbohydrate, protein, fat, vitamin, or mineral) that is in food. The body needs nutrients to function and grow.

Essential nutrient: A nutrient that is required for normal bodily functions. They're either not made by the body or can't be made in sufficient quantities to maintain good health; they must be provided through diet. The six basic essential nutrients are carbohydrates, proteins, fat, minerals, vitamins, and water.

Macronutrient (macros for short): The nutrients our body utilizes in the largest amounts, namely, carbohydrates, fat, and protein. They are used for energy and to maintain the body's structure and system.

Carbohydrates: Also called 'carbs', these are sugar molecules. The body breaks down carbs into glucose, which is the main source of energy for cells, tissues, and organs.

Protein: The basic structure of protein is chains of amino acids. They are building blocks, and every cell in the body contains protein. Protein is important for repair and growth.

Fat: Triglycerides, cholesterol, and other fatty acids store energy and have a protective function. Fat contains twice as much energy as carbohydrates or protein. Fatty acids act as messengers and support the function of protein. Certain vitamins are fat-soluble, meaning that we need fat to absorb them.

Micronutrients: Micronutrients, mainly vitamins and minerals, are needed in very small amounts. Nevertheless, their impact on our health is critical, and deficiencies can cause severe and even life-threatening conditions.

Vitamins: Vitamins are organic compounds that are essential for normal growth and metabolic processes of an organism. There are various types of vitamins, with 13 being essential. Four of the essential vitamins are fat-soluble and nine are water-soluble.

Minerals: Minerals are used to maintain body functions, including those regarding the muscles, heart, and brain. They are also important in the production of enzymes and hormones. Minerals are differentiated into macro minerals and trace minerals. In traditional literature, there are 13 essential minerals, but some sources name 21.

I'm not going to pretend that it's easy to take care of your nutritional needs and to be accurately covering your macro and micronutrient requirements. In fact, it requires a good level of knowledge, lots of dedication, and certainly planning. That is without taking any special physiological, ethical, or preferential needs into consideration. And even if we would diligently cover all the above, we still cannot be certain about the actual nutritional value of our produce and foods. This is why I always suggest supplementing! However, I will come back to this a little later.

Nutritional energy, and our happiness!

Despite what I just said, there are many areas of our nutrition that we can easily approach in a more mindful and conscious manner. Let us look at a few aspects of nutritious energy: quantity, nutritious value, and energetic quality.

Energetic quantity

The quantity of energy coming into our bodies through our food intake in comparison to our energetic needs is an important consideration for weight management. The theory here is quite simple and straightforward. We have a certain daily energy expenditure. If we consume more than we exert, our body converts energy into fat and stores it – we gain weight. If we consume less than we need, we lose weight.

To know your energy requirement, you can use the formula below:

Daily energy requirement = basal metabolic rate (BMR) x physical activity level (PAL)

Now it gets a little bit more complex, and we might have to estimate. Our BMR, sometimes called Resting Metabolic Rate (RMR), is the number of calories that our body needs to execute basic life-sustaining functions without any additional movement. This means we should never consume less food than is required to cover our BMR. Bye-bye, crash diets! Our BMR depends on our weight and, more importantly, on our body composition. This is the distribution of the different tissue types, e.g. muscles, fat, etc. Because muscles burn more calories than fat, two people of the same height and weight can have quite different energetic needs. Our body composition can be measured through a traditional (and quite accurate) caliper, which looks like an oversized tweezer, or through a bioelectrical impedance machine. There are a few more complex methods that are used in sport science and athletic training, but these two are the ones you might have access to. Even if not, you can find formulas to estimate your BMR.

Here is a good equation to estimate your BMR:

Men = 88.362 + (13.397 x weight in kg) + (4.799 x height in cm) – (5.677 x age in years)

Women = 447.593 + (9.247 x weight in kg) + (3.098 x height in cm) – (4.330 x age in years)

Whilst this is not super accurate, it will give you a good place to start. Remember, we are aiming for improvement rather than perfection.

The PAL can be established with the table below. If the lifestyle is very sedentary, I would personally recommend using a PAL of 1.2, even with light exercise, whereas you might consider 1.4 if you do not exercise but, for example, walk your dog for an hour every day and do some gardening, etc.

Activity level	PAL
Little/no exercise	1.2
Light exercise 1–2x/week	1.4
Moderate exercise 2–3x/week	1.6
Hard exercise 3–5x/week	1.8
Physical job or hard exercise 6–7x/week	2
Professional athlete	2.4

I have compared the above-mentioned formula with the results from a bioimpedance machine in several examples and found the results to be reasonably accurate, unless you are either very obese or very athletic. Basically, when you are on either outlying side of the normal spectrum, most measures might fail because their algorithms are calculating your results based on the 'normal range'.

Now that we know how much we can, and should, eat, the big question is, of course, if it matters what we eat. Can we consume our full calorie allowance in chocolate bars and candy? The answer is obviously no. The quality of our diet is extremely important if we want to support our energy, health, and well-being. Have you heard the saying, 'You are what you eat'? There is a lot of truth in that! If you are consuming a lot of 'fast food', you may expect the nutritious value you receive to be fast and short-lived. And 'junk food'? Unfortunately, just the same. What we consider junk is often made up of a lot of processed, artificially manufactured, unnatural ingredients that tend to clog up your system and provide little nutritional value aside from the actual calories (which of course are most probably far too many).

Since micronutrients, including minerals and vitamins, do not contain many calories, we can focus on the macronutrients first. Before we investigate a sensible macronutrient distribution within our daily diet, let us just remember that all macronutrients are vital and fulfill essential functions within our body. The hype about restrictive diets, such as 'low-carb', 'no-carb', 'low-cal', 'low-fat', etc., is dangerous and misleading. It is implied that these diets are healthy and that certain macros are bad for us. What is much more accurate is that there are better and less-preferable choices for each of the macronutrients. It is also a fact that the typical Western diet is high in sugary carbs, unhealthy fats, and sodium. In addition, it is overall too high in calories, with large portion sizes being considered normal. Rather than investing the time to re-learn healthy eating habits and establish a well-rounded diet, millions of people, worldwide, repeat a vicious cycle of overconsumption followed by occasional, equally unhealthy and stress-inducing, crash diets.

Somehow, hearing that a basic, normal way of eating, and by that I mean what should be normal, rather than what is typical, might be the solution to many of our health problems is less appealing than torturing ourselves with the umpteenth punishing and torturing diet.

What surprises me even more than this masochistic behavior is the passion with which people like to defend their eating habits. I seem to regularly offend many well-meaning grown-ups when I politely decline lollipops for my son because he doesn't eat much sugar (and if he does, then I would like that to be a home-baked cake for a special occasion and certainly not a lollipop that is completely void of any nutritional value and completely artificially fabricated – but that's just my choice for our family).

Food is a sensitive topic. It's personal! A possible explanation for this might stem from our ancestors and our intrinsic fear for our survival. Yes, food is survival. We need to eat. However, we are following dangerous trends with our nutritional habits and need to quickly rectify the way we nourish ourselves. There could be a whole other chapter about the effects of our overconsumption on the planet, environmentalism, and sustainability, but that is for another author to discuss. At this point, I am just inviting you to have a critical look at your eating habits and the reasons for the way you eat.

Nutritious Value

Let us come back to what a sensible macronutrient distribution looks like. Once you have established your daily calorie intake, we can follow official guidelines to split our macros. In general, it is advised that most adults should plan their diets to consist of 45–65% Carbohydrates, 10–35% Protein and 20–35% Fat. The percentages are of the previously established daily energy requirement, measured in calories.

This is a little broad, and I would always urge you to keep the protein on the high side, whether you are engaging in weight training or not. Protein is the macronutrient that requires the most conscious planning and is therefore often on the low side, unless you are eating a high-calorie diet. If you go into a convenience store or supermarket searching for a quick snack, you will easily find options that are high in sugary carbs and fats but don't contain much protein. That is why I always like to start the following calculations with the protein, keep the fat moderate, and allocate the remaining percentage to the carbohydrates. Now we need to convert the macro percentages into grams to better design our own meal plan.

Let me take you through an example based on what we have learned so far.

Sample macro calculation

A person has established their ideal daily calorie intake to be 1965 kcal.

Macro distribution:

Protein 25% x 1965 kcal = 491.3 kcal	
491.3 kcal/4 kcal = 123 gr	A gram of protein has an energetic value of 4 kcal!

Fat 30% x 1965 kcal = 589.5 kcal	
589.5 kcal/9 kcal = 66 gr	A gram of fat has an energetic value of 9 kcal!
Carbs 45% x 1965 kcal = 884.3 kcal	
884.3 kcal/4 kcal = 221 gr	A gram of carbs has an energetic value of 4 kcal!

- ➢ Daily calories: 1965 kcal
- ➢ Carbs: 221 gr
- ➢ Protein: 123 gr
- ➢ Fat: 66 gr

This is the point at which I normally hear, 'I don't want to count my calories' or 'I am not going to weigh my food!' from my clients. Don't worry if that is exactly what you have been thinking, or even if you are just feeling daunted by the thought of having to do this.

Ask yourself why you have resistance to doing this exercise. Because it's too time-consuming? Too tedious? Too much effort? Just not your cup of tea? As I mentioned before, change is simple but it is not easy. It requires effort as well as determination. But I do have some good news for you! I don't want you to measure your food forever, not even for a long time. I promise. All I need you to commit to is three days. They don't even need to be consecutive.

An argument I often hear from people that are doing reasonably well with their diet is that they want to continue following their natural, intrinsic way of eating, and to listen to their bodies to know what they need. This is great, and I absolutely encourage this approach. I would still urge you to track your food for a few days. Unless you are eating 95% of your meals at home, without any store-bought snacks, drinks, etc., you actually do not know exactly what you are consuming. And even if that's the case, your eating habits might be off, even if due more in part to the micros than the macros. Our bodies change over time, and our habits and routines are deeply affected and influenced by a lot of external factors, such as our lifestyle, routines, work schedules, kids' schedules, etc.

Trust me, this will be an eye-opening experience and help you to transform the way you eat with a long-lasting impact. Furthermore, this will give you a fallback meal plan whenever you need one. After the holidays, stressful periods at work, or times of low motivation and overeating, you will know how to get back into a healthy, energy-sustaining, nourishing way of eating. And the best thing about it? You can still eat what you like and enjoy your food, and rather than punish yourself with diets, treat your body, mind, and soul the right way!

Here is what I need you to do:

- Calculate your maintenance calories.
- Calculate your macros.
- Download MyFitnessPal (an amazing free app).

- Use a small kitchen scale to (approximately) measure your food.
- Enter all meals into MyFitnessPal.
- Optimize and modify your diet based on your results.

As I said, you only need to do this for a few days! It's important to check your intake several times a day so that you get an understanding of what you still need/should avoid toward the end of each day. MyFitnessPal also gives you the main micronutrients and will alert you if specific items are high in beneficial, or abysmal, nutrients. The app will calculate your maintenance calories for you and follow a macro distribution of 50% carbs, 30% fat, and 20% protein.

If you choose a weight loss goal, go for the slowest option to keep your calories closer to your maintenance calories. As I mentioned before, I prefer a higher protein percentage, but if you find it irritating to constantly think about your own ideal distribution, then the App's guidelines will also work and give you great results. You will quickly understand what your nutrition downfalls are and what is already going well. To optimize, you do not need to completely change your diet but rather find better alternatives. There are thousands of healthy recipes for every dish that you can think of, including desserts. Again, this is not a restricting diet, this is you finding a way of eating that suits your lifestyle, your dietary needs, and leaves you feeling energized, happy, and wholesome!

You can find many YouTube tutorials on how to get the most out of the free version of MyFitnessPal. Rather than getting obsessed with the app or calorie counting, however, I want you to simply feel the difference. Just give it a good shot and see what happens.

That's it. I just saved you lots of bucks on nutritionists, dieticians, and fancy diet drinks. Most importantly, I saved you years of frustration, feeling unwell, having a damaging relationship with food, and disliking your body. Maybe you decide that you really do not have time for this and invest in a meal delivery program, which I consider a good option. In this case, please use the knowledge you just gained to critically assess the meal plan and allow it to be a learning experience for the way you eat after. Be in charge. Know what you are doing!

Energetic quality

Now, back to the main road – the aspects of nutritious energy. We've talked about the quantity and the nutritious value; let's get into the quality. There are many food items that might fulfill our macronutrient requirements but do not add much nutritional value aside from those macros. These foods are low in micronutrients and antioxidants and often high in processed, artificial ingredients and potentially toxic substances. As always, we need to consider what our bodies are designed to do, what they can process and digest. Aside from exposing ourselves to a compromised immune system, we are adding physiological stress if we provide unnatural nutrition that cannot easily be broken down and digested. There also are a few ethical and environmental considerations around the energetic value and quality that I will talk about further down.

What is the energetic quality that is provided by micronutrients?

While macronutrients are essential for a wide variety of sustaining – as well as growth and repair – functions, many micronutrients directly affect our hormone and neurotransmitter production and availability. From an energy point of view, our macronutrient intake gives us direct energy and affects our metabolism, and micronutrients contribute in a more complex, subtle manner. Melatonin, for example, is the main hormone regulating our sleep behavior; it is therefore a key component in our energy management. This naturally occurring hormone is produced mostly in the pineal gland in the brain, from the precursor L-Tryptophan, an essential amino acid. Remember that essential, in nutrition, means that it cannot be produced by the body and needs to be consumed. Serotonin, one of the happiness hormones, is also a precursor of melatonin and also requires L-Tryptophan. You will find more information about L-Tryptophan and Serotonin later in this chapter. Before we move further into the endocrine system, the relevant micronutrients, and talk about the happy hormones, there are a few more aspects of energetic quality worth mentioning.

Ethical considerations

Our eating behavior is a personal topic, and many people have become conscious about the external, environmental, ethical, and spiritual impact their eating habits have on our extended environment. I would even argue that many are more concerned about the external impact than about the internal impact. It is, of course, a desirable development to see many individuals awakening to a broader understanding of cause and effect. If I were to only be concerned about the health applications, however, then I would have to say that it complicates things greatly. As our lives have become so much more complex, artificial, and global, anything we consume and purchase has a ripple effect throughout the globe. I do believe that it is important to make conscious, educated choices about the way we lead our lives, and that certainly includes our eating behavior. However, I do also believe that the degree to which we care is our prerogative, whatever you decide is going to be the best possible choice for you.

I will not go into a deep discussion about the above-mentioned ethical and environmental implications of the modern food industry, simply because this is not the topic or purpose of this book. I encourage you, however, to assure that your eating behavior aligns with your moral compass regarding these topics. Even if we are not making conscious decisions about our consumption, I am certain that the energetic quality is impacted by its line-up with our intrinsic beliefs and values. On a cellular level, our bodies know what is right and what is wrong.

The good news is that even small changes to our eating habits, such as reducing portion sizes and minimizing food waste, have a great impact on the environment. But even just replacing one food item each day with a similar one can substantially lower our individual carbon footprint. In a recent study in the US, it was found that substituting just one serving of daily meat with poultry saw close to a 50%

reduction in the individual carbon footprint. This means that it isn't even necessary to give up animal products to improve our environmental impact.[*]

Choosing local or regional produce and being mindful of in-season crops and vegetables is another simple step with big results. As an additional benefit of this practice, products with shorter transportation times are generally tastier, fresher, and often less exposed to toxic, harmful pesticides. Most of us are no longer used to meeting the occasional little critter in an apple or plum, but trust me, it's a good sign when it happens. Of course, purchasing locally also supports your local economy and might give better insight into farming practices and animal welfare.

Whether you chose a carnivorous, pescatarian, vegetarian, vegan, or any in-between diet, whether you go organic, hormone and antibiotic-free, kosher, halal, or a mix is up to you. But being mindful and making conscious decisions enables you to practice gratitude and respect toward what you eat. Furthermore, you respect and care for your body with the nutrients but also your mind and soul with a way of eating that supports your energy.

For myself and my son, I have decided that eating as natural and clean as possible is the utmost priority. In a world that

---

[*] Donald Rose, Amelia M Willits-Smith, Martin C Heller, Single-item substitutions can substantially reduce the carbon and water scarcity footprints of US diets, *The American Journal of Clinical Nutrition*, Volume 115, Issue 2, February 2022, Pages 378–387, https://doi.org/10.1093/ajcn/nqab338

is full of toxins and unhealthy environments, I have made a conscious decision to support our systems with light, easy-to-digest, and antioxidant-rich foods as much as possible. Especially for my son, and whilst breastfeeding, I am choosing organic products whenever possible and affordable. I do eat animal products, but I try to go hormone and antibiotic-free, as well as organic. Fortunately, for my wallet, my son has chosen to eat hardly any meat, and for his digestive health, I am very happy about that.

In 2007, I was working on Cruise Ships as a Fitness Director in the Caribbean. During that time, I was able to get great understanding and insight into the effect that different methods of food production and processing might have on the growth and development of children and teenagers. I was stunned to meet many parents who lived conscious and healthy lives that were clueless as to why their children were overweight and couldn't shed the weight. These were not the families that partook in the ridiculous midnight buffets and were regulars at the soda fountains but those who had good nutrition and exercise habits. Yet, when I met their children and teenagers, I often had to hold back my surprise at seeing their offspring physically looking nothing like their parents. The only explanation could be that the way they were eating was harming the children, more than the adults.

Naturally, young bodies are much more affected by any kind of additives added to their diet. As adults, we require nutrients to replace cells and maintain bodily functions, but children's bodies use the provided nutrition to build their growing bodies. I will not go into a discussion about whether growth hormones in meat and poultry influence humans and human development because this topic is not yet sufficiently researched. However, I would like you to consider our body's ability to deal with artificially added substances and the potential way it slows down our digestive system.

Self-harming with nutritious energy

If we want to respect, love, and honor ourselves, then we need to do this wholeheartedly and include our bodies. This involves the way we nurture and feed ourselves as well as how much activity we provide. We know that our mind's and body's well-being and health are closely connected, and we are aware that stress, sedentary lifestyles, and our diet affect us in a multitude of ways. Inappropriate habits affect us physically and mentally. However, we still lead our lives in a disconnected manner and don't consider the importance of daily habits, such as the way we eat, when it comes to our whole system.

The unpleasant truth is that if we are not conscious about the quality and quantity of our nutrition, then we are likely engaging in an act of self-harm.

When it comes to our diet, there are many ways in which we can endanger ourselves: overeating, undereating, malnutrition – just to name a few. When we hear of malnutrition, we might have images of deprived, impoverished, and starving children in developing nations in mind. But malnutrition is also common in obese populations around the world. Contemplating the energetic quality vs the energetic quantity of our diets explains this phenomenon, and this is the reason why these considerations are so important.

The highest potential for self-harming through our nutrition, however, lies in our unconscious behavior and our habitual laissez-faire attitude when it comes to our eating. Making 'exceptions' when eating out, 'treating ourselves' with a rich chocolate cake for a stressful event, overindulging (regularly) and telling ourselves that 'a little treat won't harm' are all narratives that we use to excuse our unhealthy food relationship. Many of us have grown up conditioned in some way or another to have distorted ideas about the value of nutrition and the correct way of treating ourselves through nutrient-dense food.

Take a moment to consider how food was used and thematized in your home when you were a child.

Here is a list of common statements and practices. You can tick the ones that you are familiar with and add some more that apply to you:

- receiving a treat in exchange for studying/chores/ behaving a certain way
- receiving a treat in the event of unhappiness/being physically hurt
- receiving a treat in exchange for being quiet
- a general 'You get this when you do that' attitude

- hearing adult family members say that they 'treat themselves' to something after a hard day at work or other adverse events
- hearing adult family members say that they 'need' something, e.g. 'I need my coffee', 'I need chocolate', etc.
- hearing adult family members say that the occasional treat 'won't do any harm'
- witnessing adult family members go on diets
- witnessing adult family members engage in periods of overeating (holidays, etc), followed by extreme diets
- being shamed about eating certain types of food or quantities of food (too much, too little)
- witnessing adult family members use food for mental wellness or being encouraged to do so yourself ('this will make you feel better').

Can you think of others?

-
-
-

Looking at the statements that sound familiar and true to you, which are the ones that still hold a lot of power over your personal relationship with food?

How can you change this dynamic and develop a habit of treating your body to nutritious and nourishing meals?

Make a commitment, right now, to make conscious choices about your diet and to consider each meal as an important act of self-love and self-care:

Pretty much all our problems, issues, and feelings of unhappiness originate from a place of self-destructive behavior. It is a lack of self-love, self-care, and self-prioritization that causes us to not even want to try and to belittle the importance of, as well as the power we hold over, our physical and mental well-being.

I will repeat it one more time: if you are not consciously and mindfully practicing healthy nutrition habits, then you are self-harming. There is no gray area! This doesn't mean that you can't eat chocolate, drink a glass of wine, have a pizza, or that you must engage in rigid diets. It simply means adding intention to our choices, including the less healthy ones.

Gut bacteria and our happiness!

There are quite a few sayings that we use that hint at the brain-gut connection, such as 'butterflies in my stomach', 'sick to the stomach', 'gut-feeling', 'gut-wrenching', or 'nervous stomach', just to name a few. You might have even heard that the gut is our second brain. But how influential is the function of the gut on our mental health? The gut produces a variety of important hormones, neurotransmitters, and other chemicals that promote a balanced state of mind. Seventy percent of the body's immune system resides here, and over ninety percent of our serotonin is produced in the gut.

The gut-brain axis is the pathway for bidirectional communication between the cognitive centers of the brain and the intestinal system. A healthy gut microbiome is paramount to maintaining these interactions. Although the gut does not contain the same intellectual abilities as our actual brain, the intestinal network uses the same chemicals to alert the brain when something is not right. The constant communication between these massive nerve centers, the biggest we have in our body, affects how we feel and impacts our quality of life. The second brain, in connection with the first brain in our skull, partly determines our mental state and plays a leading role in certain diseases.

The gut does much more than handle our digestion and occasionally giving us a nervous pang. The second brain, which is officially known as the enteric nervous system (ENS) or intrinsic nervous system, is an autonomous part of our nervous system, consisting of neural circuits that control motor function and local blood flow as well as modulate endocrine and immune functions. The ENS spreads from the lower part of the esophagus to the rectum and is embedded in the wall of the gastrointestinal system. The second brain contains around 100 million neurons, which is more than we have in the peripheral nervous system or the spinal cord. This vast number of neurons in the ENS allows us to 'feel' the inside of our gut and be affected by it. This part of our body is equipped with its own reflexes and senses and can control the gut behavior without input from the brain. Researchers have found that it is a highly complex and evolved system and, therefore, has many more uses and functions than merely taking care of waste removal.

In fact, it was discovered that around 90% of the information traveling along the vagus nerve, the primary visceral nerve, was signaling from the gut to the brain and not vice versa. This leads to the assumption that a lot of our emotions might be heavily influenced by the nerves in our gut. Whilst any gastrointestinal upset would certainly sour our moods, even our everyday emotional well-being may be affected by messages from the brain below to the brain above. Due to these findings, the effect of electrical stimulation on the vagus nerve is currently being researched as a useful treatment for depression.

The close interconnectedness of our two brains explains why traditional depression treatments that target the mind also often affect the gut. As mentioned earlier, over 90% of our serotonin is found in our intestines. The most commonly used antidepressants, called selective serotonin reuptake inhibitors, SSRIs for short, increase the availability of serotonin and, therefore, often provoke gastrointestinal issues as an unwanted side effect. A common, unpleasant symptom, irritable bowel syndrome, which affects more than two million people in the US, could be regarded as a 'mental illness' of the second brain, given its close relation to stress and accompanying lifestyle behaviors (as well as the high levels of serotonin in the gut). But we are also discovering that the serotonin that is produced by the enteric nervous system may play a role in other, more surprising, diseases; it has been found that certain drugs that inhibit serotonin release are linked to the development of osteoporosis. We will learn more about nutrition's effect on our hormonal balance and its impact on our mental well-being in the next section, but it is fair to say that mental disorders always affect the gut and vice versa, at least to some extent. Taking care of our gut bacteria and making sure that our system is as 'clean' and 'unclogged' as possible is just one of the many ways we can promote better mental, and of course physical, health.

Our gut microbiome, consisting of around 40 trillion bacteria, is a well-balanced, fine-tuned system. The best way to restore and maintain a healthy gut environment is by eating a fresh, balanced, and non-refined diet.

Here are five science-based ways to improve your gut bacteria:

1. Eat a diverse range of food

Did you know that an estimated 75% of the world's foods are produced from 12 plant and 5 animal species? In fact, the traditional Western diet does not provide many varieties and is rich in sugar, fat, and calories. It has been found that diets in rural regions are often more diverse in a variety of plant sources.* In line with this, the gut microbiome diversity is greater in the populations of rural Africa and South America

---

* De Filippo C, Di Paola M, Ramazzotti M, Albanese D, Pieraccini G, Banci E, Miglietta F, Cavalieri D, Lionetti P. Diet, Environments, and Gut Microbiota. A Preliminary Investigation in Children Living in Rural and Urban Burkina Faso and Italy. Front Microbiol. 2017 Oct 13;8:1979. doi: 10.3389/fmicb.2017.01979. PMID: 29081768; PMCID: PMC5645538.

than in the urban populations of Europe and the United States.

There are around 300 to 500 different species of bacteria in the gut, which all have specific health contributions and require different nutrients. The more species of bacteria in our gut, the more health benefits they may contribute. Therefore, a diverse microbiome is considered a healthy one.

2. Eat lots of fruits, vegetables, beans, and legumes

Vegetables, beans, legumes, and fruits are the best nutrient source for a healthy and varied gut bacterium because of their high-fiber content. Our bodies cannot digest fiber; however, certain bacteria in our gut can, and this stimulates their growth.

High-fiber foods include:

- raspberries
- artichokes
- green peas
- broccoli
- chickpeas
- lentils
- whole grains
- bananas
- apples.

A 2016 study found that a high-fiber diet was able to minimize the growth of disease-causing bacteria.[*] This demonstrates that a diet rich in fruits and vegetables doesn't just encourage the growth of beneficial bacteria (also called bifidobacteria) but also actively decreases the harmful ones. Bifidobacteria aids in the prevention of intestinal inflammation and increases our overall gut health.

3. Eat fermented foods

Fermentation is a process in which the sugars contained in food is broken down by yeast or by bacteria. Fermented foods, like plain yogurt, can benefit the microbiome by enhancing its function and by actively reducing the number of disease-causing bacteria in our intestines.

Examples of fermented foods are:

- yogurt
- kefir
- kombucha
- labneh
- sauerkraut
- kimchi
- miso.

---

[*]   Klinder A, Shen Q, Heppel S, Lovegrove JA, Rowland I, Tuohy KM. Impact of increasing fruit and vegetables and flavonoid intake on the human gut microbiota. Food Funct. 2016 Apr;7(4):1788-96. doi: 10.1039/c5fo01096a. PMID: 26757793.

Many fermented foods contain lactobacilli, a beneficial type of bacteria. Lactobacillus is a type of probiotic. Research has found that individuals who eat a lot of yogurts have more lactobacilli and less enterobacteria – a bacteria that is associated with inflammation and certain chronic conditions.[*]

4. Eat prebiotic and probiotic foods

Prebiotics are substances that the microorganisms in our bodies utilize to grow and live, giving rise to the associated health benefits. The best researched and documented health benefits come from the non-digestible oligosaccharides fructans and galactans, which are basically dietary fiber.[†]

Good sources are found in:

- asparagus
- garlic
- onions
- wheat

[*]   Lisko DJ, Johnston GP, Johnston CG. Effects of Dietary Yogurt on the Healthy Human Gastrointestinal (GI) Microbiome. Microorganisms. 2017 Feb 15;5(1):6. doi: 10.3390/microorganisms5010006. PMID: 28212267; PMCID: PMC5374383.

[†]   Beserra BT, Fernandes R, do Rosario VA, Mocellin MC, Kuntz MG, Trindade EB. A systematic review and meta-analysis of the prebiotics and synbiotics effects on glycaemia, insulin concentrations and lipid parameters in adult patients with overweight or obesity. Clin Nutr. 2015 Oct;34(5):845-58. doi: 10.1016/j.clnu.2014.10.004. Epub 2014 Oct 20. PMID: 25456608.

- tomato
- barley
- honey
- rye
- milk (human and cow's milk)
- chicory.

In addition to this list, most vegetables, legumes, and fruit contain some type of prebiotics. Aside from promoting a varied gut bacterium, certain prebiotics have also been found to decrease insulin, cholesterol, and triglyceride levels in obese individuals.

You might have heard of probiotics as 'good' gut bacteria. Probiotics are live microorganisms that have health benefits for our bodies. The most studied species, Lactobacillus and Bifidobacterium, create a more favorable gut environment and support healthy immune function. There is promising research investigating the supportive benefits on organ health and even our mood and mental well-being.

5. Eat foods rich in polyphenols

Polyphenols are a large group of plant compounds that have been found to have many health benefits for our bodies, including a decrease in oxidative stress, blood pressure, cholesterol levels, and inflammation. More than 8000 different polyphenols have so far been identified.

Because polyphenols are not efficiently absorbed and digested by human cells, they reach the colon, where they are digested by gut bacteria.*

Foods rich in polyphenols are:

- cocoa and dark chocolate
- grape skins and red wine
- green tea
- almonds
- onions
- blueberries
- broccoli.

The science of neuro-gastroenterology is investigating the workings and impact of the second brain in relation to our physical and mental health. Thus far, the relationship between the enteric nervous system and many diseases has not been systematically reviewed, like in the case of the central nervous system. However, the already-discovered benefits of a healthy gut microbiome are certainly enough to aim for a diet that helps to maintain, balance, and restore our gut function. Researchers in the field already assume that psychiatry will need to expand its treatments to the second brain to maximize treatment outcomes and benefits.

---

* Cory H, Passarelli S, Szeto J, Tamez M, Mattei J. The Role of Polyphenols in Human Health and Food Systems: A Mini-Review. Front Nutr. 2018 Sep 21;5:87. doi: 10.3389/fnut.2018.00087. PMID: 30298133; PMCID: PMC6160559.

As with many of the other topics in this book, we need to keep in mind that our advanced and modern lifestyles are what are removing us further from our natural way of living. With that, a variety of new issues and imbalances occur, which will have to be, once again, tackled in a holistic manner. The gut and its impact on our overall health is certainly a great example of this theory.

The endocrine system, nutrition, and our happiness

Food affects mood! In addition, our mood influences how we eat as well as our cravings. When we are feeling balanced and in a positive mood, we tend to make better choices. Unfortunately, we have an increased need for nutrient-dense food when we are stressed or feeling low, which is when we might make worse choices and indulge in unhealthy 'comfort food'.

Our mental health and our mood are closely related to our micronutrient intake because these micronutrients help to regulate and manage our endocrine system. If the endocrine system is not working at its best, we experience hormonal imbalances.

In the chapters about stress, we already learned a fair bit about the role hormones and neurotransmitters play in stress regulation and mental health. When add the second brain into the picture and consider that the way we eat affects our gut health, which in turn affects our hormonal balance, which affects our happiness, we can better appreciate how impactful this holistic point of view can be, if applied wisely.

The micronutrients that have been found to be most relevant and important for our mental well-being are vitamins B1, B2, B5, B6, B12, calcium, vitamin D and E, folic acid, iron, magnesium, selenium, and zinc.

Here is a list of these micros, their function, and the best food sources.

Micronutrient	Mood-related function	Source
Vitamin B1 (Thiamine)	• Acts as a coenzyme in the synthesis of neurotransmitters • Can mimic the action of the neurotransmitter acetylcholine in the brain	• Fortified breakfast cereals • Pork • Fish • Beans, lentils • Green peas • Enriched cereals, bread, noodles, rice • Sunflower seeds • Yogurt
Vitamin B2 (Riboflavin)	• Is a co-enzyme of proteins, needed to metabolize fatty acids • Has antioxidant properties	• Dairy milk • Yogurt • Cheese • Eggs • Lean beef and pork • Organ meats (beef liver) • Chicken breast • Salmon
Vitamin B5 (Pantothenic acid)	• Involved in the synthesis of neurotransmitters • Contributes to the structure and function of brain cells	• Fortified cereals • Organ meats (liver, kidney) • Beef • Chicken breast • Mushrooms • Avocados • Nuts, seeds • Dairy milk

Micronutrient	Mood-related function	Source
Vitamin B6 (Pyridoxine)	• Plays a fundamental role in the synthesis of neurotransmitters	• Beef liver • Tuna • Salmon • Fortified cereals • Chickpeas • Poultry • Some vegetables and fruits, especially dark leafy greens, bananas, papayas, oranges, and cantaloupe.
Vitamin B12 (Cobalamin)	• Involved in maintaining the myelin sheaths surrounding nerves • Supports synthesis of neurotransmitters	• Fish • Meat • Poultry • Eggs • Dairy products
Vitamin D (Calciferol)	• Linked to Serotonin production • High concentrations of Vit D receptors in many areas of the brain	• Cod liver oil • Salmon • Swordfish • Tuna fish • Orange juice fortified with vitamin D • Dairy and plant milk fortified with vitamin D • Sardines • Beef liver • Egg yolk • Fortified cereals
Vitamin E	• Protects cell membrane from damage from free radicals	• Wheat germ oil • Sunflower, safflower, and soybean oil • Sunflower seeds

Micronutrient	Mood-related function	Source
		• Almonds • Peanuts, peanut butter • Beet greens, collard greens, spinach • Pumpkin • Red bell pepper
Calcium	• Important for the release of neurotransmitters • Helps to control signaling between cells	• Dairy (cow, goat, sheep) and fortified plant-based milk (almond, soy, rice) • Cheese • Yogurt • Calcium-fortified orange juice • Winter squash • Edamame (young green soybeans), tofu made with calcium sulfate • Canned sardines, salmon (with bones) • Almonds
Folic Acid	• Cofactor for the conversion of tryptophan into serotonin and tyrosine into norepinephrine/ noradrenaline • Involved in the synthesis of neurotransmitters	• Dark green, leafy vegetables (turnip greens, spinach, romaine lettuce, asparagus, Brussels sprouts, broccoli) • Beans • Peanuts • Sunflower seeds • Fresh fruits, fruit juices • Whole grains • Liver • Aquatic foods

Micronutrient	Mood-related function	Source
Iron	• Cofactor to produce energy in the brain • Involved in the production of neurotransmitters	• Nuts • Dried fruit • Whole meal pasta and bread • Iron-fortified bread and breakfast Cereal • Legumes (mixed beans, baked Beans, lentils, chickpeas) • Dark leafy green vegetables (spinach, silver beet, broccoli) • Oats • Tofu
Magnesium	• Important for the transport of ions such as potassium and calcium • Important for cell signaling	• Dark, leafy greens • Nuts and seeds • Fatty fish such as salmon and tuna • Soybeans • Avocado • Banana • Dark chocolate • Non-fat or low-fat Greek yogurt • Brown rice
Selenium	• Part of the antioxidant enzymes that protect from free radicals	• Brazil nuts • Pork • Poultry • Fish • Shellfish • Eggs • Cottage cheese • Cooked mushrooms

Micronutrient	Mood-related function	Source
Zinc	• Important for neuron function and transmission	• Meat • Shellfish • Legumes • Seeds and nuts • Dairy products • Eggs • Whole grains • Dark chocolate

Aside from these important micros, there are a few other key nutrients that we should be aware of. The feel-good hormone Serotonin plays a key role in fighting off anxiety and depression. It is so powerful that the most prescribed group of anti-depressant drugs (SSRIs – selective serotonin reuptake inhibitors) work by increasing serotonin levels in the brain. Serotonin (5-hydroxytryptamine or short 5-HT) is a neurotransmitter that can also act as a hormone. It carries messages between the central nervous system (in the brain) and the peripheral nervous system (throughout the body). Serotonin plays crucial roles in influencing memory and learning; overall happiness; and regulating sleep, body temperature, appetite, and sexual behavior. A lack of serotonin is linked to anxiety, depression, and manic behavior disorders.

Serotonin is made from the essential amino acid tryptophan and is found in large quantities in the cells lining the gastrointestinal tract. Only around 10% is produced in the brain. As tryptophan is an essential amino acid, it cannot be made by our bodies and must be obtained through our nutrition.

As mentioned above, a healthy gut bacterium is an important foundation for many biological processes, and certainly for well-balanced serotonin levels. In addition, we can eat foods that are rich in the amino acid tryptophan to encourage the production of serotonin.

Foods rich in tryptophan include:

- sunflower seeds
- spirulina
- cod, salmon
- soybeans
- potatoes
- eggs
- oats
- milk
- chickpeas
- wheat
- cheese
- beef
- quinoa
- chickpeas
- chicken/turkey.

Another popular feel-good hormone, dopamine, might also be positively affected by our nutrition; however, research is inconclusive. We cannot eat dopamine, but it is produced via the amino acid l-tyrosine, which is non-essential. It is naturally produced from another amino acid called phenylalanine. However, it is also found in many foods, such as cheese, chicken, turkey, fish, dairy products, and generally in most high-protein foods.

Tyrosine assists in the production of several chemicals. Aside from dopamine, it is also involved in the making of adrenaline and noradrenaline, thyroid hormones, and melanin. Research with tyrosine supplementation has not been fully conclusive; however, there is some evidence that increased levels of tyrosine raise the availability of these neurotransmitters and, in turn, help to improve memory as well as performance and resilience in stressful situations.

In a 2013 study, it was established that tyrosine supplementation significantly improved memory function during a mentally demanding task in comparison to a placebo.* This finding was reproduced in a few different study designs.

In addition, tyrosine supplementation seems beneficial to improve symptoms of sleep deprivation and may even reverse mental decline. Whilst supplementation may not be necessary for everyone, topping up on the tyrosine-rich food groups mentioned above can certainly assist in a well-balanced body and mind environment.

Another nutrient that has recently been researched for its potential mood-improving properties is Omega-3 fatty acid, particularly eicosapentaenoic acid (EPA). EPA is one of several omega-3s and is found in cold-water, fatty fish, like salmon. It is available in fish oil supplements, together with docosahexaenoic acid (DHA). It has been

---

* Colzato LS, Jongkees BJ, Sellaro R, Hommel B. Working memory reloaded: tyrosine repletes updating in the N-back task. Front Behav Neurosci. 2013 Dec 16;7:200. doi: 10.3389/fnbeh.2013.00200. PMID: 24379768; PMCID: PMC3863934.

long anecdotal that fish oil has beneficial effects on our mental well-being, as well as improving cardiovascular health; studies are now adding proof to this theory. In a scientific meta-analysis from 2016, it was concluded that the treatment effect of fish oil supplementation was comparable to the effect of traditional antidepressant medication.

The greatest benefits were observed in a combination of fish oil supplements and antidepressants. It appeared that higher doses of EPA were preferable. The exact working mechanisms of omega-3s on mood and mental health are still unclear, but it is speculated that omega-3s have a positive effect on serotonin and the serotonin receptors in the brain.[*]

The link between happiness and nutrition

Taking care to consume the correct number of calories, macronutrients, and micronutrients might appear challenging at first. Fortunately, however, most of the important nutrients can be found in similar groups of food. Clean, fresh, healthy eating can have tremendous benefits on not only our body but also our mental well-being and, therefore, happiness!

---

[*]   Mocking RJ, Harmsen I, Assies J, Koeter MW, Ruhé HG, Schene AH. Meta-analysis and meta-regression of omega-3 polyunsaturated fatty acid supplementation for major depressive disorder. Transl Psychiatry. 2016 Mar 15;6(3):e756. doi: 10.1038/tp.2016.29. PMID: 26978738; PMCID: PMC4872453.

Whilst our grandparents got away with a less mindful approach to eating because of their higher physical activity levels, as well as the lesser availability of refined, artificial products, we can no longer afford this tactic. Our life expectancy has drastically increased due to medical knowledge and expertise, yet we often fail to implement the same knowledge to prevent fatal diseases and mental health problems. You now have the power to make a change for your body and your mind!

Time to take a look at your existing eating habits!

☞ Exercise:

Take a moment to answer the questions below.

What is your biggest issue when it comes to nutrition (quality, quantity, regularity, etc.)?

What is the reason for these behaviors?

What will you do, starting today, to change this?

✷ Key points:

✷ The effects of nutrition: Everything we intake is what the body uses to build its future iterations which, in turn, will affect how we feel in our body. It has been scientifically proven that nutrition has a direct effect on our mental well-being.

✳ How much food: Based on our age, our size, and our daily energy expenditure, there is a unique food requirement for everyone. This amount is an excellent bit of information we can use to tap into a more holistic way of eating.

✳ Nutrition energy: It's important for us to consider the amount, the type, and the distribution of our nutrients, among other things, when thinking about our diet. A conscious food relationship, taking all of this into account, is what helps us tap into the potential of our nutrition.

✳ The second brain and its role in the body: While the gut doesn't quite function like the brain itself, it has a large influence over how we feel and, in turn, how we think about our surroundings. Many hormones are produced in the gut, and the gut and the brain have a strong rapport between them.

✳ Foods to help build a happy gut and mind environment: Given the gut's influence over our brain and overall state of being, it is important to consider foods that have a beneficial effect on our gut biome, such as fruits, vegetables, and fermented foods, as well as remembering to consume a healthy variety of all.

How movement affects our mental health

It is no secret that physical activity boosts our mental well-being. Many people use exercise to positively affect their feelings and emotions. Whether to boost energy or relax, exercise can greatly impact our lives in a multitude of ways beyond physiological health. Physical activity releases feel-good hormones; boosts our metabolism; improves sleep quality and our sleep cycle; helps with energy management; nurtures healthy lifestyle habits, including nutrition; and increases our confidence. In fact, regular activity has been found to relieve anxiety, depression, and anger.

There are a few facts regarding exercise and activity, however, which are often neglected. For starters, we often consider exercise primarily as a tool to alter the way we look. But the reality is that physical activity is so important to our overall health that not engaging in it should be considered a dangerous habit. This fact calls for a significant mindset shift, from considering exercise as a 'recommended' behavior toward regarding it as a mandatory one. While, in the past, the World Health Organization would provide guidelines for the recommended daily amount of physical activity, we now consider not walking an hour every day as high-risk behavior.

The human body is designed to move. In fact, every 'body' should be moved; however, not everybody has to exercise! Whether you choose to exercise or not depends on your specific goals, desired appearance, and (medical) needs.

A structured exercise regime will allow you to manipulate your physical looks as well as your fitness levels and improve your health significantly, but we can't neglect the benefits of increased overall activity. Movement, in comparison, is a more random, unstructured, event that can happen through a variety of activities such as living an active lifestyle, housework, physically demanding work, etc. To be reminded of how active we are supposed to be, just observe a young child or watch a documentary about rural tribes and their lifestyles.

Exercise was not a necessity for our ancestors but has become popular and important due to our increasingly sedentary lifestyles. However, unfortunately, it is an unrealistic expectation to balance the damage done by 15 hours of near immobility with one hour of exercise (that is within 24 hours). On top of that, many of us are sedentary most of the week and work out only two to three hours in seven days.

So, whether you train or not, increasing your overall activity levels should always be a conscious first step toward improved health and well-being. I will go so far as to argue that increasing your activity by as little as 30 min every day will show a significant improvement in your well-being, energy levels, sleep behavior, and health. The even better news is that breaking up those 30 mins into smaller intervals and spreading them throughout the day might provide you with even greater benefits.

Here's how:

- ✓ Adding small movement breaks into your workday can significantly improve your posture and help with neck and back pain.
- ✓ Every time you get up to move, you increase your blood circulation as well as your metabolism. Your elevated

heart rate will continue to stay slightly increased for a few minutes until after you sit back down.

✓ Movement increases the oxygenation in your body, including the brain. This helps to increase focus, concentration, memory, and sensation of overall well-being.

✓ Taking short movement breaks has been found to act as a de-stressor, which can relieve tension and anxiety.

✓ Your breathing is likely to deepen whilst you are moving, helping you to feel energized and refreshed.

I will remind you about the importance of planning and the conscious programming of your body and mind several times in this book, and consistently increasing your daily activity is not going to happen accidentally! So go ahead and schedule six 10-minute movement breaks; put them in your calendar. Yes, that equals 60 minutes, not 30 minutes as I proposed earlier. Chances are, you will skip some or only move for five minutes. Overplanning is always a great option to make sure you hit your target and it helps you not to stress if you can't leave your desk at one of the scheduled time slots. And if you do achieve the full 60 minutes, then you are only winning.

Don't skip this, schedule your movement breaks now!

There is a wide range of activities you can do in these ten minutes. If you decide to go for a toilet break, that is a fair option. But maybe you can go to the bathroom located furthest away, maybe even on another floor. You can refill your water bottle or get a tea/coffee, to name a few, but again, try to take the most complicated route to the kitchen – climb a few sets of stairs and, in general, get into the habit of adding steps wherever you can. Depending on the weather, you can aim to make it outside for a few breaths of fresh air; maybe you have a roof terrace or balcony you can take advantage of. If you prefer to stay close to your workstation, get up and move through a short stretch and movement routine.

If you are scheduling your movement breaks at home, you can even add a quick mini-workout. This can be something as simple as a quick bodyweight workout, consisting of Squats; Superman's; or (Wall) Push Ups, Dips, and Crunches. These basic exercises have lots of variations and target the whole body. You can even do them when watching TV. Whilst writing this book, I aimed to perform one set of 20 repetitions every two to three hours. This has definitely helped me to prevent back pain and sore hips – remember my personal story in the 'About' chapter?

If you need inspiration, just go for a quick search on YouTube. There is a real wealth of easy-to-follow workout routines fitting all time-budgets, fitness levels and desired outcomes.

In 2008, I had my first big corporate engagement, developing a workplace wellness strategy for a big company in Germany. At that time, leading health insurance companies were offering rewards and discounts to those being physically active and partaking in well-being programs and initiatives; hence, there was great buy-in and attendance from all levels of seniority. After delivering a workshop on the importance and benefits of movement breaks, I was called into a meeting with one of the senior leaders. He surprised me with a fantastic idea; he had asked the IT team to develop a screensaver program that would come on at set times during the workday. All the work was saved, but employees couldn't use their computers for ten minutes. We decided on specific messaging and health tips that were displayed after a 30-second countdown, once in the midmorning and once in the midafternoon. What a revolutionary idea! You can imagine that initially there was much concern and even disapproval from employees and co-workers. We made sure to validate the effectiveness of the program with questionnaires and found that after the first 30 days, employees felt improvements in their productivity, enjoyed the social interaction during their movement breaks, came up with creative ways to take advantage of these ten minutes, felt encouraged and empowered to promote their own well-being, and appreciated their employer's initiative. There was an overall improvement in back pain as well as stress levels. If you are reading this, maybe you have the possibility to start a similar movement at your workplace and change your and your co-workers' experience for the better. I would love to hear from you – please reach out and tell me all about it!

Higher-intensity exercise certainly provides a multitude of additional health benefits and should not be neglected if possible. But I am sure that we can all agree that we tend to shy away from even starting a routine because we often take an 'all or nothing' approach. And whilst more exercise might lead to more gains, no movement certainly leads to rapidly decreasing health and well-being. In short, doing less with consistency is better than doing more infrequently.

Exercise is not just about improving our aerobic fitness and increasing muscle mass. As mentioned before, a good workout regime will likely improve your physical health and appearance, trim your waistline, increase your energy levels and libido, and even lengthen your life expectancy, but there is more. Let's explore the factual benefits that physical activity has on our mental well-being.

Research has shown that people who exercise regularly seem to do so because it provides them with an enormous sense of well-being. Those 'addicted' to physical activity report higher energy levels throughout the day, improved sleep quality at night, increased cognitive function and memory, more alertness and creativity, and increased feelings of relaxation, positivity, and a sense of calmness.[*] Regular exercise can have a profound impact on depression, anxiety, and ADHD symptoms.

As already mentioned, even modest amounts of physical activity can help improve overall mood and make a real difference. No matter what your starting age or pre-existing fitness level might be, you can learn to use exercise as a powerful tool to deal with mental health problems; improve your overall outlook on life; boost your energy, motivation, and drive; and live happier. Unfortunately, the importance in, and potential for, treating mental health conditions with exercise is still often neglected and underestimated;

---

[*]   Deslandes A, Moraes H, Ferreira C, Veiga H, Silveira H, Mouta R, Pompeu FA, Coutinho ES, Laks J. Exercise and mental health: many reasons to move. Neuropsychobiology. 2009;59(4):191-8. doi: 10.1159/000223730. Epub 2009 Jun 10. PMID: 19521110.

however, recent research suggests physical activity to be a powerful potential intervention in mental health care.[*]

The improvements in overall mood and well-being are contributed to the exercise-induced increased blood-circulation, its effect on the hypothalamic-pituitary-adrenal axis, and its physiologic reactivity to stress (the HPA axis is also discussed in the chapter on 'Stress'). It appears that the positive exercise effect is mediated by the communication between the HPA axis and several regions of the brain, such as the limbic system, which affects motivation and mood; the hippocampus, which is important for memory function, as well as mood and motivation; and the amygdala, which is the control center for the fear response in reaction to stress (also discussed in the chapter 'Stress'). There are a variety of mechanisms that account for the mood-boosting effects of movement, including antioxidation, neuroinflammation, vascularization, and energy adaptation. On an endocrine level, there are three major neurotransmitters and neuromodulators that are known to be affected by exercise: dopamine, noradrenaline, and serotonin.

Dopamine

This feel-good chemical directly impacts the central nervous system and plays an important role in the brain's reward system by reinforcing feelings of pleasure that we experience when we engage in rewarding activities.

---

[*]   Callaghan P. Exercise: a neglected intervention in mental health care? J Psychiatr Ment Health Nurs. 2004 Aug;11(4):476-83. doi: 10.1111/j.1365-2850.2004.00751.x. PMID: 15255923.

Dopamine is often referred to as the 'pleasure hormone', but it doesn't actually produce pleasure. Rather, it emphasizes feelings of pleasure by linking certain actions and behaviors to sensations of pleasure. Dopamine is part of our intrinsic reward mechanism, and when it is produced by our brain in response to something we do, we feel good and want to do more of whatever it was we were doing.

Aside from just making us feel good, dopamine directly impacts important neurological, cognitive, and behavioral functions, such as movement, arousal (also part of the stress response), regulation of certain hormones and glands, thoughts, and emotions. It affects everything from our memory function to our thinking ability. However, individuals can be affected by, and respond to, dopamine differently. It can be difficult to detect a dopamine imbalance, but it will likely affect our physical and mental health. Both too little and too much can cause significant problems.

Low dopamine levels might cause symptoms such as low energy, low sex drive, mood swings, difficulty sleeping, anxiety, constipation, loss of balance, tremors, forgetfulness, inability to focus, withdrawal, low self-esteem, and weight change.

High dopamine levels can initially lead to positive feelings; however, they can also cause aggression, impulsiveness, increased risk-taking behavior, substance addiction and addictive behavior, stress, intense competitiveness, and sleeplessness.

Dopamine imbalances can not only have serious physiological and mental health implications but also be a contributor or side effect of diseases. Decreased levels can be seen in neurodegenerative diseases such as Parkinson's, wherein the nerve cells responsible for dopamine production and release are dying.

Research suggests that ADHD is linked to a decrease in the activity of dopamine in the prefrontal cortex, the region of the brain that is responsible for executive functions such as planning, decision-making, and working memory. This decrease in dopamine activity is thought to contribute to the characteristic symptoms of ADHD, including inattention, impulsivity, and hyperactivity. Stimulant medications, such as methylphenidate and amphetamines, are commonly used to treat ADHD. These medications work by increasing the activity of dopamine in the brain, thereby improving executive functions and alleviating the symptoms of ADHD. The role of dopamine in ADHD is complex, and more research is needed to fully understand how dopamine dysfunction contributes to the disorder. However, current evidence suggests that dopamine plays an important role in the development and maintenance of ADHD, and medications that target dopamine activity have been found to be effective.

Addictive behavior can be considered a dopamine-triggered, conditioned response to certain stimuli, such as alcohol or drug abuse, smoking, gambling, etc. It is unclear why some people are more likely to develop addictive behavior patterns, but it likely is due to pre-existing differences in dopamine circuits. A review from 2013 suggests exercise as an alternative treatment method for addiction.* It has been implied that regular exercise remodels the reward system over time, which leads to increased levels of dopamine and dopamine receptors. These positive changes may even repair the neurological damage caused by substance abuse.

Major Depressive Disorder (MDD) is one of the most common and debilitating mental health diseases and is characterized by persistent feelings of sadness, hopelessness, and a loss of interest in everyday activities. One of these symptoms is 'anhedonia', the inability to feel pleasure, which is related to a disturbance in dopamine levels. Decreases in dopamine can occur following stress and often appear in combination with certain types of depressive disorders. Dopamine is one of several neurotransmitters that is thought to be involved in the development and treatment of MDD. Certain antidepressant medications, such as bupropion and some atypical antipsychotics, work by increasing the activity of dopamine (rather than serotonin) in the brain. These medications are thought to be particularly effective for individuals with MDD who experience anhedonia and show other symptoms associated with low dopamine activity.

Dopamine also appears to be involved in the pathology of schizophrenia. This debilitating mental disorder has a multitude of symptoms ranging from disorganized speech

---

*   Lynch WJ, Peterson AB, Sanchez V, Abel J, Smith MA. Exercise as a novel treatment for drug addiction: a neurobiological and stage-dependent hypothesis. Neurosci Biobehav Rev. 2013 Sep;37(8):1622-44. doi: 10.1016/j.neubiorev.2013.06.011. Epub 2013 Jun 24. PMID: 23806439; PMCID: PMC3788047.

and behavior to delusions and hallucinations. Whilst some patients are more disabled by this disorder than others, most will depend on lifelong treatment and care. Relevant research suggests that this neurodevelopmental disease has a strong dopamine influence. After four decades of research, it is apparent that deficiencies and excess dopamine can lead to symptoms. The 'dopamine hypothesis of schizophrenia' was one of the first theories for the disorder. It suggests that a dopamine imbalance is responsible for schizophrenic symptoms because it plays an important role in defining our sense of reality. Too much or too little might consequently result in delusions and hallucinations. This theory, which dates to the 1960s and 70s, is still considered valid and true; however, the role of other neurotransmitters is now also more widely investigated.

Noradrenaline

Also called norepinephrine, this chemical is created in our nerve endings and helps us to stay alert and focused. This neurotransmitter is tricky, and we need just the right amount. Too much can easily cause anxiety, but too little might result in symptoms of depression. As a neurotransmitter in the spinal cord and the brain, noradrenaline constricts blood vessels to maintain blood pressure during stress and increases attention, alertness, arousal, and affects our sleep-wake cycle, memory, and overall mood. It's essentially a stress hormone and impacts the areas of the brain that are controlling action and attention. It is, therefore, also connected to the fight-or-flight response and can trigger the related physiological symptoms, such as increased blood flow to the muscles, released glucose for energy, and increased heart rate.

Reduced levels of noradrenaline might result in low energy levels, declined alertness, difficulty concentrating and paying attention, and decreased cognitive ability. Because of its pronounced effect on large areas of the brain, noradrenaline is commonly used to treat psychiatric disorders. A newer class of antidepressant medication, serotonin-norepinephrine reuptake inhibitors (SNRIs), work by inhibiting the reabsorption of serotonin and norepinephrine by nerve cells, which makes more of these neurotransmitters available in the brain. SNRIs seem to be more effective in their antidepressant action than the, previously more common, selective serotonin reuptake inhibitors (SSRIs).

Like dopamine, noradrenaline also plays an important role in patients with ADHD. Whereas low levels of norepinephrine negatively impact a person's ability to focus and concentrate, it has been found that children with ADHD show elevated levels of norepinephrine in their urine sample; this is linked to higher levels of hyperactivity. The urine collection method is not a fully validated testing procedure and not used to diagnose psychosomatic disorders; however, there is sufficient evidence for a correlation between urine samples and noradrenaline levels in the brain.

Serotonin

This extremely important neurotransmitter has already been introduced in a few chapters ('Stress' and 'How nutrition affects mental health'). To recap, serotonin greatly impacts our mood, anxiety, and stress, and gives us feelings of happiness and well-being. During the developmental years, serotonin promotes the healthy development of normal anxiety behaviors and coping strategies. In adulthood, balanced serotonin levels are required to reduce anxiety-like behaviors. Serotonin is involved in the communication between nerve cells. After being released, serotonin binds to receptors of the neighboring cells and transmits signals that affect a wide range of psychological and physiological processes. It is involved in the regulation of sleep, appetite, digestion, and mood.

The link between low serotonin levels and depression, anxiety, and other mood disorders has been well established. This knowledge is used in the pharmaceutical treatment of these mental health concerns (SSRIs and SNRIs, see above).

When our serotonin levels are normal and balanced, our mood is regulated, and we feel content and satisfied, it can further reduce the effects of stress on our mind and body, making us more resilient and equipped to handle stressful events. Serotonin helps to regulate the physiological stress response and even down-regulates the production of stress hormones such as cortisol. In addition, serotonin enhances our social behavior and increases our ability to bond, show empathy, and our overall social cognition. This, in turn, can lead to better relationships and social support, which is said to have a positive impact on mental health and happiness.

Because of its effect on stress responses, Serotonin promotes healthy melatonin production and sleep behavior, which is crucial for mental and physical health.

These three major neurotransmitters and neuromodulators, dopamine, noradrenaline, and serotonin, are so relevant in the treatment of mental health issues that they are commonly used in pharmaceutical treatments; however, a conservative approach of prevention and treatment through exercise has not been widely established yet. Knowing that it is most probably quite challenging to create, or start, a consistent exercise routine when one is experiencing symptoms of depressive disorders isn't a reason not to try establishing one. If anything, it makes the habit of a regular, active lifestyle even more important.

There are other hypotheses that propose explanations for the beneficial effects of physical activity, including distraction, social interaction, improved confidence and body image, self-care, and self-efficacy. Structured group training programs have been investigated as potential treatment modalities; however, lifestyle adjustments focusing on increased moderate intensity throughout the day are appropriate for most people and can be easily integrated into even the busiest lives. Studies have found that thirty minutes of moderate activity, such as brisk walking, for three days per week will not only improve fitness levels, exercise tolerance, blood pressure, weight management, and perceived energy levels but also provide mental health benefits such as better sleep patterns and quality, increased mood, feelings of happiness and being well-balanced, and decreased stress levels. These thirty minutes do not need to be continuous; three 10-minute sets are said to be equally useful, and, in addition, provide physiological benefits as mentioned earlier. As this topic finds heightened interest in research, there are a variety of studies with different exercise protocols and durations, hence finding the one that fits best into your individual schedule and time availability, as well as the one that is the most enjoyable and fun to you – this is probably the best place to start. Even a small commitment might be able to relieve symptoms of mild-to-moderate depression as effectively as antidepressant medication – in a natural, sustainable way, without the side effects!

Exercise is a powerful tool for numerous reasons. In addition to previously discussed neurotransmitters and neuromodulation, it promotes several changes in the brain, including neural growth, decreased inflammation markers, and new circuitry activity that promotes feelings of well-being and calmness. Movement also positively impacts our physiological stress responses by relaxing the muscles and encouraging us to breathe better.

Endorphins

Other significant depression fighters that are released through exercise are endorphins. These chemicals are proteins that act as neurotransmitters. Endorphins are inhibitory neurotransmitters, meaning they block other messaging signals. They are particularly good at blocking pain signals.

Research has found twenty different types of endorphins. Beta-endorphins, which were believed to cause a 'runner's high', are the most thoroughly investigated.[*] These endorphins are created by our pituitary gland and then released into the bloodstream. Because they cannot cross the blood-brain barrier (BBB), however, it is now understood that beta-endorphins cannot cause feelings, including the feeling of euphoria called the 'runner's high'. The BBB is a barrier that keeps substances that are circulating in the bloodstream from entering the central nervous system and the brain. Scientists are, therefore, now researching the possibility of hormones called endocannabinoids being responsible for the 'runner's high' effect. These hormones are also released during exercise and are natural versions of plant-based drugs, such as cannabis. More investigation is required to confirm the exact workings of endocannabinoids as well as potential other chemicals that are contributing to the euphoric sensations during exercise.

The primary function of endorphins, the pain release, is an immediate response to a painful sensation and is generally short-lived. In addition, however, they also trigger the release of other hormones, such as dopamine, which has a longer-lasting 'feel-good' effect.

Endorphins regulate our immune and inflammatory response and have a calming effect; they prevent the immune system from getting triggered unnecessarily, as otherwise could be

---

[*] Sprouse-Blum AS, Smith G, Sugai D, Parsa FD. Understanding endorphins and their importance in pain management. Hawaii Med J. 2010 Mar;69(3):70-1. PMID: 20397507; PMCID: PMC3104618.

the case during high-intensity exercise. The same applies to stress responses; endorphins help our body to respond appropriately to stressors, including the lowering of body temperature and slowing down the heart rate.

Committing to exercise

No matter how easy I make squeezing physical activity into your busy schedule sound, you might have already come up with a long list of reasons why it isn't going to work for you. Not everyone has engaged in sport and exercise growing up, and you might have never experienced the feel-good sensations after a workout. And if that's the case, then exercise can appear challenging, uncomfortable, taxing, and ultimately not worth the effort. Barriers to exercising are real – especially if you are experiencing mental health issues. However, you now know, at least in theory, why you really should find a way to make it work. Remember, not moving is a high-risk behavior for your overall health and well-being. So how can you overcome the obstacles?

Obstacle #1: Time

As we have learned, fortunately, you do not need as much time as you might have thought. However, if you still don't see this working out for you, try being a 'weekend warrior'. A recent study found that people who squeeze one or two sessions into the weekend experience almost the same mental health benefits as those working out more often. Don't let your busy schedule hold you back from reaping the benefits of physical activity – they are just too good.

Obstacle #2: Feeling exhausted

The last thing you probably want to do when you are tired, exhausted, stressed, and feeling rushed is to work out. But even if this feels contradictory, exercise is a powerful energizer. Physical activity can dramatically reduce sensations of fatigue and increase energy levels. What's more, these effects are instantaneous.

Obstacle #3: Feeling overwhelmed

The thought of having to add yet another obligation when you're already feeling overwhelmed might certainly feel like a bad idea. Working out might not seem practical, or even possible. However, try to change your mindset to one of being in control of your schedule and prioritizing self-care. Can't make it to the gym? No problem – start with small home workouts and activities that can be done anywhere, even with your kids around....

Obstacle #4: Low self-esteem

If you are your own worst critic, you might engage in some negative self-talk that will sabotage your movement journey. We all know those inner voices that tell us all kinds of untruths about how we aren't good enough and how we're going to fail – so why try? It's time for a new way of thinking about yourself and your body. Accomplishing even the smallest milestone will improve your body confidence and improve your self-esteem.

Obstacle #5: Pain

If you have pre-existing health issues, weight problems, injuries, or illnesses, then consult a physician prior to engaging in any exercise program. However, keep the benefits of short, moderate-intensity workouts in mind and don't let your condition stop you from experiencing the benefits. Where there is a will, there is certainly a way, and you deserve all the feel-good hormones and pain-reducing effects of movement.

Obstacle #6: Motivation

This is a big one. You knew that exercise is good for you before reading this book. Now you know quite a bit about the how and what. But unfortunately, just because you know something, doesn't mean you are feeling it, right? Many of us find it hard to motivate ourselves to exercise at the best of times. Add to it anxiety, depression, stress, and other mental health issues and it might appear impossible to find the motivation to get up and do something – anything. Here are a few steps that can help you slowly build up intrinsic motivation:

- ✓ Start small! Set yourself tiny, achievable goals, even just one minute whilst watching TV.
- ✓ Find an accountability buddy! Maybe someone around you is in the same boat, and it would prove much easier to find consistency together. In addition, you get the benefits of social interaction, and it multiplies the fun.

✓ Use your high-energy times! Learn when your energy is at its peak and, if possible, plan your workouts during that time.

✓ Find activities you enjoy! There is no point in attempting to do something you dislike because you believe it to be the most beneficial. The benefits are in the fun.

✓ Reward yourself! You will already be rewarded by the benefits of exercise, but to help your motivation, promise yourself an extra treat – this could be a nice hot bath, an extra episode of your favorite TV show, or even new workout clothes after sticking to your plan for some time.

We live in a time of exponential growth of the 'metabolic syndrome', which describes a variety of health conditions such as increased high blood pressure, excess body fat and weight, elevated cholesterol and/or triglyceride levels, and high blood sugar. These symptoms occur together, increasing our risks for type 2 diabetes, heart diseases, and stroke. The high prevalence of metabolic syndrome is a result of our diets and sedentary lifestyles. As is the case with our diet, our grandparents did not have to worry too much about adding physical activity into their lives. We, on the contrary, are experiencing high risks because of our inactive lifestyles. The more methods of 'convenience' we develop and are made accessible to us, the less we are forced to move and be physically active. This requires us to make active choices and to be conscious about the way we exercise, move, and live our lives. With the ongoing growth of our cities and subsequent increasing distances to be covered, a motorized way of transportation is often the only option. The need for efficiency and time management forces many people to take advantage and outsource tasks and duties, such as shopping, housework, and washing their car. Therefore, movement does not happen accidentally anymore for many of us and has to be a consciously planned and executed event.

You have the knowledge, you have the tools, and now it is your turn to put those learnings into action!

☞ **Exercise:**

Take a moment to assess your current situation:

What is your biggest issue when it comes to movement (lack thereof, irregularity, sedentary lifestyle, etc.)?

What is the reason for these behaviors?

What are your biggest obstacles and how can you overcome them?

What can you commit to, starting today?

What is your biggest takeaway from this chapter?

* Key points:

* Sedentary lifestyle as a high-risk behavior: As a society, we tend to view exercise as an option that doesn't affect us much whether we choose it or not. Given the plethora of benefits that small amounts of mild movement have on our well-being and the damaging effects that non-movement can have on our bodies, not being physically active is less of a harmless option and more accurately described as a high-risk behavior.

* The 'feel-good' feeling of exercise: Exercise has a direct effect on our physical and mental state of being. Dopamine, Noradrenaline, and Serotonin are the big three neurotransmitters when it comes to exercise. They all have a role to play in our hormonal ecosystem as we begin to move our bodies.

* Exercise and movement – the imagined hurdle of entry: With all the different exercise styles and trends, it might seem difficult to get started. It's simply a matter of finding what works for us, what we can maintain consistently, and what helps us feel good; we need to build our own personal relationship with exercise.

IV : Training Your Happiness Muscle

When I started my career in the fitness industry, I was immediately fascinated by anatomy and rehabilitative training. I was drawn to the way the human body functions and the way everything is connected. I felt that by understanding a few core principles, anatomy made intuitive sense. Of course, I might be one of few who thinks like this, but for me, there is a logical order in the way muscle chains and muscle slings function and how we can restore the sensitive balance of stability and mobility that our bodies need in order to perform at their best. Believe me, I could go on for quite some time on this subject.

Whilst I was working as a Personal Trainer, Rehab Coach, Strength & Conditioning Specialist, and Nutrition Coach, I quickly understood that once a person trusts you with their body and their physical health, they will often feel comfortable sharing their deepest secrets. This is a curious phenomenon that has been experienced by many other Trainers and Coaches whom I've spoken to about this.

Despite being aware of the obvious need people felt to share their emotional baggage and to request my uneducated advice, I used to be quite skeptical toward the profession and role of 'Life Coach'. It all seemed a bit vague, and I didn't appreciate the importance of having someone teach you about better ways of living your life.

Much later, however, after around 12 years in the Fitness and Wellness industry, I decided to investigate different Life Coaching programs. My main objective was to improve my clients' motivation and help them to stay on track to achieve their goals. The course that I was immediately attracted to was based on neuro-scientific findings and promised to facilitate the client's ability to create new neurological pathways. Much like the case of anatomy and physiological sciences, here was another methodology that fascinated me.

The best, and initially most surprising, aspect of Result Coaching was that all the training principles that I'd encountered for our skeletal muscles applied to the brain! The ideas and concepts of Exercise Science are so relevant to the way we can train, stimulate, and even rest the brain that I was in familiar territory and felt right at home. Again, it all made intuitive sense.

Along the journey of human existence, some smart people (likely the Egyptians around 4,000 years ago) introduced structured, physical fitness and aerobics programs and made exercise a thing. Brain training, however, has been around for less than 100 years. But the sort of brain training I am referring to is primarily used to enhance our intellectual ability, not our well-being and lifestyle management. It is only in recent years that we have been becoming more aware of the powerful mind-body connection and its effect on our overall well-being. We're slowly beginning to understand that we cannot separate physical and mental health any longer if we want to take full advantage of our human potential.

So why do we need to train our Happiness muscle? In exercise lingo, there is a saying: 'If you don't use it, you'll lose it'. This describes the muscle atrophy that occurs after a certain time of physical inactivity. In other words, if you don't encourage your body to maintain muscle mass, it will get rid of it. The older we get, the faster this happens. Does this rule apply to our metaphorical, yet all-too-real, Happiness muscle? You bet!

If you have not been happy for a long time, then your brain might no longer produce the feel-good chemicals, and your neurological wiring for happy thoughts and feelings might have been replaced by the not-so-positive ones. You will need to slowly wake these processes up and get them going. And guess what; you might even get sore along the way. Just as your muscles would from exercising, your brain might hurt and resist change. Your brain, like the rest of your body, gets comfortable and lazy doing the same things, thinking the same thoughts. So initially, your brain might not want to produce serotonin and the other happy hormones. It might actually tell you that you are running just fine on all the stress hormones that you have floating around in your system.

As discussed in the chapter 'What is Stress', we can get addicted to the cascade of stress hormones, just as we can get easily addicted to sugar. Both are harmful, but we still get trapped. Once you have become too accustomed to these stress hormones and the associated feelings with them, you might easily perceive rest and relaxation as uncomfortable sensations. You might find yourself being bored, not stimulated, and lethargic. Then you might become restless and crave some stress and excitement. We need to slowly prime our system to recognize and re-learn the value and positive effects that come with rest and relaxation. Slowly introducing happiness back into our life takes some structure and planning, just like with exercise. It's ok if this is a new concept for you; we tend to expect 'happiness' to just happen. However, happiness is a practice and a lifestyle.

Happiness is a learned behavior, like brushing your teeth.

To help your body and mind recognize the benefits of your new mindset and lifestyle, however, it is also important to assure that we maintain a level of excitement. The high levels of hormones felt previously, because of stress, need to be replaced with other high levels of hormones, but this time we'll focus on the feel-good ones.

I am telling you this because it is extremely important to remember these facts when you find yourself struggling along the journey. When everything inside you is telling you to go back to the way things were before. That you were doing ok. That things weren't that bad. That others are much worse off. True, it could always be worse, but you started this journey because you wanted more than 'ok'. Because you knew that you deserve more.

So, keeping exercise principles and physical training theories in mind, we will start slow. We will prime our nervous system to experience happiness again, learn how to create little pockets of happiness, and find a sustainable way of reaching your goals.

What is Happiness?

When I talk about happiness in my workshops, I almost always have participants in the audience that are not fully comfortable with the idea of aligning their life to the pursuit of ultimate happiness. This is no surprise, as many of us have been conditioned to think of our own happiness as selfish. We might have been taught that service to others should be our main goal in life. I certainly do not disagree with that at all. However, I am sure we can all agree that we can only make others happy when we are content within ourselves. Making others happy will then, in turn, add to our happiness even more.

We cannot pour from an empty cup. Nourishing our own feelings of happiness, exploring these sensations, learning what fills our cup, and cultivating our own happiness lifestyle is what will make us better at serving those around us. When you begin to tune into this complete experience of happiness, fully immerse yourself in this sensation on an emotional, intellectual, spiritual, biological, and cellular level; then the positivity you radiate to those around you will be on a level that you might not even be imagining right now. Maybe you know people who have mastered the art of happiness already. If you do, do you remember how you feel in their presence? How their aura of happiness effortlessly encapsulates you and their positivity rubs off on you? How you can bathe in their light? That is the art of giving!

Another important aspect of giving, however, is the way we lead by example. I think that this is something that we don't consider enough. Imagine a parent, living their life in service to their family. They work hard, long hours to provide the best possible life for their children. They also support their own parents, as this is our duty. Maybe they sometimes make it to the gym but otherwise hardly take time for themselves. We all know many people like this, and maybe this is you – always hustling, always making sure that ends are met, everyone is provided for, and everyone is taken care of. At the end of the day, you are exhausted and don't have the energy to do anything apart from trying to relax in front of the TV. Or maybe there isn't even time for that because you are preparing the school bags for the kids or answering some never-ending work emails. You fall into bed, pick up your phone and mindlessly scroll through social media because you need some time for yourself. You fall asleep too late, maybe waking up several times because your mind can't switch off. You wake up exhausted. You tell yourself this is what you have to do. Your environment supports that thought because you know many that are in the same boat. That's just how it is, right?

Now here is the most important question: Is this what you want for your children? Because the harsh truth is that this is what you are teaching them. This is what they will likely aim to achieve for themselves. We all say that we want our children to be happy. But we need to take ownership of the example we are setting and the message we are sending out. If you want to break the hustle cycle and teach your children and your environment to lead conscious, aware lives, then there is no other way than to start with your own lifestyle, leading by example.

Do you want to be remembered for being that happy, radiant person or for always being hard-working?

Becoming comfortable with Unhappiness!

Everything in life needs to be in balance, and to every yin there is a yang. Where there is happiness there is unhappiness, and we can only be truly balanced and aligned when we are comfortable not only with being happy and joyful but also with being sad, angry, emotional, in a state of feeling low and unmotivated, etc. From a young age, we might have been taught that it isn't ok to not feel positively and that we need to fight and overcome those negative feelings as soon as possible. There are emotions of shame, inability, and weakness that create a fear of being depressed and unhappy. Hence, many of us spend our time in fake happiness and do not allow ourselves to linger and feel our unhappy emotions. Despite, or rather in addition to, everything I wrote above, I believe that it is extremely important to explore our full range of emotions, to get to know them, to meet them, and acknowledge the normality of all these feelings.

There is a persistent lack of acknowledgment of what I like to call the 'mental cold'. If we have a physical cold, most of us will not panic. We might be annoyed, but we will simply try to get some rest, take some vitamin C, and maybe a Panadol if needed. We recognize that our body needs to recover. The range of lingo we have for mental health, however, does not really provide much more than 'mental health' or 'mental illness'. Mental health is often seen as a constant, Zen-like, meditative, happy state, and mental illness is a serious, scary condition that we certainly do not want to experience. But the truth is that 'mental colds' are normal and healthy! Like with a physical cold, they build our resilience and make us stronger.

If you find this contradictory to what I wrote earlier, just consider the comparison to the fitness level of a person. When we believe someone to be fit and athletic, we don't expect them to be running a race all the time. We know that the person will rest, get sick, have recovery times, or maybe have an injury at some point. Yet, we still consider the person to be fit, even during their rest times. That is who they are. It is exactly the same with our mental fitness; you are still a happy person, living your happiness lifestyle, even on the days when you are feeling less motivated and allowing yourself to mentally rest.

Happiness is a choice!

Happiness does not just happen by accident. Happiness is a choice and a learned behavior. It is also not a one-time decision but, rather, a daily commitment. We are all happy at times, but when we decide to pursue a happiness lifestyle, we need to be aware of our thoughts, our feelings, and our reactions, and we need to stay in control of how we feel when things don't go exactly as planned. This is where the hard work begins.

The first step, however, is not to cultivate happy feelings. The first step is to create a mindset whereby we take complete responsibility and charge over our emotional reactions. We need to make a choice to no longer blame other people, events, and circumstances for the way we feel. So, before we move on, take a moment to check in with yourself, perhaps deep in the layers of your subconscious mind. Is there anyone you are holding responsible for any hurt, trauma, or past experiences? Is there any pain that you are holding on to, whether from a long-gone or the more recent past? Any event that you are using as an explanation for your current emotional state? Is there any past rejection, any past statements, or any old exchange that is still affecting you today?

If there is, then take a moment, right now, to let this pain and suffering go. Enable yourself to move from a past of pain, hurt, and rejection into the present moment and the promise of a glorious future filled with love, joy, abundance, and happiness. Don't worry if you are not yet ready to do this, just read on and be patient with yourself.

Letting go never means that we agree with the actions of the past. We all have the right to deem whatever has happened to us as right or wrong. However, if you disagree with something that has happened to you, let's say twenty years ago, and you are still letting this event control you, then you are the only one responsible for your present suffering. If someone mistreated you, did you wrong, and you are carrying it with you for the rest of your life, you have empowered that person to not only hurt you in that specific moment but forever! Letting go means taking back control. It means no longer being a victim but to free yourself and choose your own life experience.

Something that I tell myself, and frequently tell all my clients, is that people do something for themselves and not against you. It is us, by holding on to pain and suffering, who turn an event into a personal attack. What we feel is not because of what someone else did to us but because of what we think about what they did. Our emotions are not about these other people or situations but about how we chose to think about them.

Happiness is easy when the circumstances around us are smooth and simple. Creating a happiness mindset means to enable a positive state of mind even when the situations are tough and not favorable, when people treat us in a way we weren't expecting, or when something happens that we did not imagine possible. We need to remember that the power of a situation is what is outside of us, but the power to interpret and to react to this event is within us. Other people have the power to say what they believe is right, to do as they believe is right, and we have the power to believe what we think is right. The one mindset shift we need to start developing is to move from a life of blame to a life of personal responsibility and ownership.

'When the going gets tough, the tough get going.' – I do not use this saying except when it comes to our happiness mindset. However, it is not the tough who keep going in their pursuit of happiness – it is the resilient!

Reminding ourselves that we are the creators of our own happiness also means accepting that we are equally responsible for our unhappiness and suffering. This might sound harsh, but it's the truth. We tend to blame events and circumstances. We do this subconsciously, many times, throughout the day. It begins with the way we speak and express ourselves. 'I am stressed because of ...', 'I am upset because of ...', 'I am angry because of ...', and 'I am hurt because of ...' are all statements that enable a situation. We are not feeling the way we are feeling because of anything other than our choice to respond to something in a certain negative way. Yes, there is a stimulus that leads us to react, but it is our choice how we react in response to this stimulus. Just think about how some people just cannot be happy, even when something beautiful happens. Others, on the contrary, manage to be happy even in poverty, misery, and hardship. This shows that the situation does not make the emotion but, rather, our internal response. Surely we can all remember a personal example, a time when we were so stuck in negativity that no matter what happened it was not enough to make us open ourselves back up to positivity.

All of this is, of course, no guarantee for our happy-ever-after. So, to those of you who now cringe and want to shout: 'No one is always happy; that is just not normal.' – I agree. But the way I see it, life will throw stuff at us, no matter what we do. There will be plenty of external reasons for unhappiness. We will experience loss, death, suffering, betrayal, hardship, and more. Because of this unfortunate fact, there is really no reason for us to create internal unhappiness. People will do unjust things, speak to us in a hurtful manner, but fortunately, we can decide to keep the power within ourselves. This is our choice.

We can begin this simple mindset shift toward empowerment by observing our choice of words. As I mentioned earlier, we tend to use language that makes us dependent. It's not only our reactions that we make contingent on event but also our desires and needs. For example: 'I need my coffee in the morning.' This little sentence, or thought, has already made your experience depend on a certain thing. How will you feel when your coffee maker suddenly stops working and you can't have that cup of coffee? You might have thoughts like, 'Well that is just a great start to the day. Let's see what else goes wrong.' There is nothing wrong with having coffee in the morning. We merely need to shift toward a language that keeps us in control. Replace 'I need my coffee in the morning' with 'I chose to have a coffee in the morning.' Boom! You have just become the master of your experience and are no longer depending on it! If we allow ourselves to be a victim of the circumstances, to feel a certain way because of something or someone, to need something to be satisfied, then we cannot take ownership of our happiness.

☞ Exercise:

Write down three dependent statements that you think, or say, regularly (e.g. I need something sweet in the afternoon, I need my glass of wine in the evening, I cannot live without pizza) and formulate your new, empowered statement.

Dependent statement #1:

_____

Empowered statement #1:

_____

Dependent statement #2:

_____

Empowered statement #2:

_____

Dependent statement #3:

_____

Empowered statement #3:

_____

Practice using your empowered statements as often as possible. You will likely become aware of many more 'I musts', 'I needs', 'I have tos', 'I cannot do withouts' that you're telling yourself. Let go of all of them and allow yourself to step into your full potential as a creator. You create your own experience. I like to put Post-its with helpful reminders on my bathroom mirror. As I am writing this, my Post-it says: You create your reality!

Most of us have conditioned ourselves since our early childhood to depend on certain needs to be covered. The truth is that a child's brain is, in fact, wired to detect if certain needs are met, which go beyond being fed and watered to things like being caressed, held, and loved. These are primal survival instincts that run deep. But we, as adults, can make the switch from our infant needs to a conscious assessment of our current situation. As you are reading this book, chances are that right now you are safe, secure, and not experiencing life-threatening circumstances. Yet we tend to spend our time either emotionally stuck in the past or scared of hypothetical dangers in the future.

Because of our natural inclination to worry, and to create worries where there are none, you might intellectually agree with what you have read so far but still often fall back into your old thought patterns. This is perfectly fine. Just make the decision, today, to steadily move toward your happiness mindset and practice using your empowered language. Very soon, this will become your new, natural way of living.

Once you have mastered the everyday happiness language, you will experience the benefits of your mindset control in more severe situations. You will be able to differentiate between the body and the mind. You know the saying, 'mind over matter'? What we often do is place matter, body, over mind. 'I am not happy because I have a cold.' We let ailments of the body control our happiness. If we have a little cold, we have a horrible day, and we are bitter and upset. We say, 'The weather is depressing; I am feeling low because of it.' Yet, on the other hand, there are many people that are terminally ill or suffer a chronic condition and are still vibrant, light, and happy. Yes, I have told you a lot about the mind-body connection. And yes, many diseases will affect your hormone balance. Chronic pain will affect your mental well-being and challenge you in many ways. I have been there and I still remember the devastating effect of chronic pain. But even if it might be hard, you can still choose to be happy in mind and at heart.

Happiness is freedom!

Happiness, ultimately, is emotional independence, but also physical, social, and financial independence. Cultivating your happiness mindset means freeing yourself from dependence on circumstances and even people. Happiness is within us. It is knowing that when someone treats us badly, they are not doing it to us but are acting out on their own internal unwellness and unhappiness. They are simply showing us their state of mind; they are showing us that they are emotionally hurting – their behavior and words reflect their pain. It is not a reflection on, or reaction to, us.

Most of my clients reach a defining moment in their personal growth journey when they are ready to finally let go of that one big pain they have been holding onto. Often, this moment is not a highly emotional, tear-filled one but, rather, a peaceful, content, and calm release. Many of the situations and feelings that needed to be released have been holding power over the person for many years. It was the same in my personal experience. I had held a grudge against situations from my childhood for at least 25 years. I explained my behavior and my emotions based on events far in my past. Not only that, I even went so far as to let these circumstances define me and become part of my character. 'I am like this because of that.' I became a master of enabling the past to hold a tight grip on my present experience and thought that the future would certainly be a continuation of the previous experience. I was basically living in the past. I do not remember a certain moment when that changed, but I did have a specific experience when I realized that it had happened. For the first time in many years, I was confronted with a person from my past, and I remember clearly thinking, 'You do not control me.' I was at peace. I felt sympathy for that person and their suffering, but I was emotionally independent from them. I was free.

What others might have done to us might be horrible, and terribly wrong, and it is somebody else's mistake. However, what we often do is hold on to hatred, to shame, to suffering, to pain, and this is harm we inflict on ourselves. Yet you do not have to engage in this self-harming behavior any longer. All it takes is your decision to free yourself. This never means that we approve of what others did to us. We merely acknowledge that we do not have control over others' actions. Instead, we take full ownership of our own emotional response.

'I chose to hate for 25 years, and now I choose not to let this feeling of hate control me any longer' – this has been an exceptionally challenging but important statement for myself.

☞ **Exercise:**

What is yours? What can you release right now? What will bring you freedom?

Write it down!

Assisting my clients in creating this feeling of liberation and self-empowerment for themselves is possibly one of the most rewarding experiences for me. The understanding of this happiness concept truly is the foundation for everything else in this book.

Is happiness just a chemical reaction?

Emotion theorists suggest that there are six basic emotions we are born with, namely, fear, disgust, anger, sadness, surprise, and happiness. Happiness is not tangible or concrete, so it can be defined as a state of mind. The question of whether happiness is just a chemical reaction is philosophical and has no answer. We have learned a lot about the physiological creation of happiness and the impact of neurotransmitters – those that can enhance and even create positive feelings. Happiness, and stress alike, can be reflected in our brain chemistry and the brain's physiology, but it is not always clear if physiology impacts the chemistry or vice-versa.

There have been multiple studies that have shown that people can change their brain through different practices, such as meditation. This verifies that we can actively produce happiness, and, as a result, the chemicals that are associated with it. In the previous chapters, we have also learned how we can encourage the production and release of these happiness neurotransmitters. Therefore, whatever the chicken and egg situation might be, we have a lot of control, whether it be on our mindset, our physiological body, or our nutrition.

The seven happiness habits

Once we have established our sense of control and freedom, we can take advantage of the research in the field of positive psychology, which has established the following habits of happy people.

- ✓ Relationships: Those with a healthy social network are happier and more balanced. Quality over quantity is what you want to aim for.
- ✓ Acts of kindness: Being kind, engaging in community service and voluntary acts is highly beneficial for our own happiness.
- ✓ Exercise and physical well-being: As we learned in the previous chapter, physical activity greatly impacts our mental well-being and can even lower the risk of or treat depression.
- ✓ Being in the zone/flow: We experience flow when we are challenged but feel well-equipped (have the skills) to master the situation at hand.
- ✓ Spiritual engagement: There is a close link between spiritual practices and happiness. Spirituality and religion are closely connected to finding greater meaning.
- ✓ Strengths and virtues: Studies have discovered a close link between the recognition of our strengths, as well as using them for the greater good, and happiness.
- ✓ Positive mindset and gratitude: A positive and grateful mindset results in positive emotions, a greater sense of belonging, and lower rates of stress and depression.

✴ **Key points:**

✴ Our relationship with happiness: We've been taught to treat the prioritization of our own happiness as selfish – it's meant to be a secondary thing. However, I'm a firm believer that we can only make others happy when we ourselves are happy. Remember that you can't pour from an empty cup.

✴ Breaking cycles of dependency: When we say things like, 'I need coffee in the morning', we begin to create patterns of dependency with how we relate to our world. Try something like, 'I would like a cup of coffee this morning' instead.

✴ The external world vs the internal reaction – we have the control: There are aspects of this life that we can't control. It's inevitable that we will experience suffering and discomfort. However, how we respond to these events and moments is completely within our power. With an understanding of our stress response, we can actively guide ourselves through times of hardship in a way that doesn't leave us burned-out and strained.

✴ Choosing happiness: Happiness is a choice. The first step is to create a mindset whereby we take complete responsibility and charge over our emotional reactions. We stop blaming others, events, and circumstances for the way we feel and take ownership of our internal experiences.

 Why is change so difficult?

The topics of mindfulness, positive thinking, and mindset shift have gained so much popularity in the recent decade that the subject has become almost a cliché. With all the information and lectures available to us, shouldn't we all be floating around in a Zen-like state? And yet, depression, anxiety and stress disorders continue to rise. It appears that knowing about a topic theoretically does not automatically translate into a behavioral change.

The CNN branding campaign 'Facts First' claims that 'once facts are established, opinions can be formed.' This sounds logical, but, unfortunately, this appealing statement is not verified by research. In contrast, neuroscientific and cognitive psychology studies consider the opposite to be true; we seem to form our opinions and beliefs based on emotions such as fear, contempt, unhappiness, and anger rather than relying on facts. New information and truths often fail to change people's minds.

This is a phenomenon that I can absolutely subscribe to from my professional experience. I witness, on a regular basis, how hard it is for my clients to change their mindsets and behaviors when they are confronted with concepts and ideologies that run counter to their intrinsic beliefs. This applies even when the person desperately wants the proposed change and intellectually knows that they will benefit from it, maybe even need it to live a happier, more satisfied life.

Our world view, our opinions, beliefs, and paradigms begin to form during childhood and are strongly influenced by the cultural context in which we grow up. However, much earlier than that, with the beginning of neural brain activity, the neurological pathways in the brain shape according to every incoming bit of information, stimulus, and sensation, making each of our brains completely unique. No two people on this planet have the same brain landscape, and, therefore, no two people on this planet think the same. Our worldviews and beliefs get reinforced throughout our lives by our social connections, the media and literature we consume, and our experiences, as well as by our physiological behavior, hormonal balance, and neurotransmitter availability. This influences how we think about ourselves as well as our interactions with the outside world. In short, it is who we are.

Therefore, for most of us, having our opinions and beliefs challenged feels like a personal attack on our identity and can cause us to get defensive and want to protect our position. Whilst it is a natural defense response to resist changing our mind, we can learn to get better at it.

In an ideal scenario, homo sapiens, which, by the way, is Latin for 'wise man', would be able to evaluate new facts based on evidence and then be able to change their view accordingly, if necessary. However, as we discussed above, this is not how it seems to work in real life. One reason for this is a phenomenon called cognitive bias. Cognitive bias occurs when we let our own construction of reality, rather than objective information, dictate our behavior. In psychology, it is considered a deviation from rationality in judgment. We will talk about this more in 'Our thoughts create our reality'. Rather than reevaluate our beliefs based on evidence and facts, we might categorically reject the incompatible idea when cognitive bias kicks in. This is called 'belief perseverance' in psychology. Every one of us can fall prey to this ingrained way of thinking.

Our brain can easily feel threatened when we are presented with new facts, whether via conversations, the news, or social media. This unknown information will get easily rejected when it doesn't align with our personal and political identity. Our core beliefs, and the paradigms that we have established to be true, are deeply anchored in our subconscious mind, and we have concluded, over time, that they are what is keeping us safe. Any attack on these thought models, therefore, is initially perceived as dangerous, threatening, and unsafe. We might even experience a backfire effect as we strengthen our original thoughts and beliefs to firmly reject the confronting facts.

Another form of bias, confirmation bias, describes our natural tendency to interpret information to match up with our existing beliefs and even seek out facts that confirm and support our position. This happens subconsciously and will often cause errors in our judgement because we can no longer look at a situation objectively. We tend to interact with like-minded groups and people, choose media that aligns with our thoughts, and stay away from challenging interactions, all to keep ourselves feeling safe and supported in our opinion.

Our brains are hard-wired to protect us and our perceived reality, which can lead to an instinct to hold on to our beliefs and perceived truths, even if they are misguided. In addition, most of our paradigms were established to keep us safe and were probably required and necessary at some point in our lives. Letting go of them can feel threatening to our subconscious mind. In the chapter 'Master your paradigm shift', we will talk about practical ways to help our brain to feel safe in the process.

Before we attempt to change our thinking and develop new mindsets, however, we need to acknowledge that our brains have not yet fully adapted to the dramatic lifestyle changes mankind has undergone in the past thousands of years. Whereas our ancestors were exposed to regular life-threatening situations, most of us no longer are. But back then, it was an important survival skill for our brains to be negative, pessimistic, and to always expect the worst outcome. Whilst we are now living more and more consciously, and with an advanced understanding of our psychological and neuropsychological function, our brains will still follow rudimentary and primitive processes to protect us. In addition, our brains are not (yet) equipped to deal with the constant sensory overload that we are exposed to, which results in high levels of perceived stress. This, in turn, causes the brain to be even more cautious and concerned.

To make matters worse, being right and winning an argument, even if just in our mind, leads to the release of two hormones that you are now quite familiar with (if you have read 'What is stress?'): dopamine and adrenaline. Being right is exciting and feels good. It can make us feel invincible, and we will most probably want more of it.

But there are even more hormones involved. Remember the effect stress has on our thought processes. In a stressful, challenging situation, our brain releases cortisol, which can hijack our advanced thinking ability, reason, and logic – the executive functions of our brain. Our fight-or-flight response is triggered and we are deep in our primal behavior instincts. At this point, we have lost all ability to listen and evaluate new information correctly. This might be more commonly observed in a heated conversation between two or more people, but you might be undergoing the same patterns, internally, when stress arises as you try to create a mindset shift for yourself.

But even with the existence of cognitive biases and our intrinsic brain biology, we can find ways to bypass these natural habits. We can practice keeping an open mind and allowing ourselves to learn new things on a regular basis. Forcing ourselves to argue discussion points from two opposing points of view teaches us to change our perspective. Having open conversations and focusing on listening and understanding, rather than talking, with people that don't share our opinions can help us develop our ability to assess information objectively. These exercises are by no means meant to change all your beliefs and worldviews but are merely a step to prepare you for when you experience that your paradigms are holding you back. When you are ready to make a mindset shift, you will have the cognitive ability and practice to do so more smoothly.

Creating a mindset change is simple, but it is not easy!

Despite everything I mentioned above, there are a wealth of positive thinking techniques and exercises out there, leading to the common misconception that it should be quite easy to change our mindset and acquire a positive go-getter mentality. The easier all the promoted behavioral changes sound, the guiltier we end up feeling when, yet again, we fail at consistently putting them into action.

One major disadvantage of perceiving something as easy is that we often don't put the necessary resources toward achieving it, for example, effort, time, consistency, and mental energy. Creating change is, in fact, difficult, mainly because it happens outside of our comfort zone. This applies whether we are talking about physical or mental goals. You will probably already agree with this statement when it comes to physical exercise, but just consider that your mental training follows the exact same principles. To achieve change, we cannot remain the same, we cannot think the same, and we cannot do the same. The steps, however, are simple. Acknowledge what you are currently doing/thinking, assess whether this will lead you to your goals, decide what will get you there, and do it! You will find this process explained in the chapters 'Master your paradigm shift' and 'Creating an emotional connection to your goals'.

Creating a mindset shift needs action!

If you were happily nodding away whilst reading the past few pages, then you are a big step closer toward achieving your individual happiness mindset. However, please keep in mind that simply understanding a concept will not automatically create any change. If you have ever read a self-help book (maybe even this one) and skipped all the exercises, you probably understand exactly what I'm saying. And trust me, I have done it, telling myself that I would get back to the exercises later. Yeah, right! This is the exact equivalent to purchasing a gym membership and never going. Did you know that gyms live off the, so-called, ghost members? It is estimated that around 30% of gym memberships go unused, with most members failing to ever visit the gym after three to six months. Unfortunately, we will not get any change from simply buying the membership, reading the book, or glancing over articles. We need to put our determination and thought energy into it and commit.

Self-blame prevents change!

Whenever you work toward change, it is important to have a loving and kind attitude toward our previous decisions, mindsets, and paradigms. We need to hold our old selves with love and appreciation. As we have learned, all our beliefs have developed for good reasons. They were part of our social construct, needed to protect us, or simply were what was right at that time. Often, when I work with clients on a paradigm shift, they engage in some harsh self-criticism. But this kind of toxic self-talk only prevents us from moving forward. In fact, it is only because of our past decisions that we can look back and assess them. Everything you have done has led you right here, reading this book, creating your happiness lifestyle. It is only because of your previous decisions that you are now in the position to look back and realize that, in hindsight, you maybe could have made a better decision. However, know that you did not have the knowledge or resources to do so in the past. We live, we develop, and we grow. That is the essence of change.

Creating a mindset shift will have you live in the unknown!

I have given you the psychological and neuroscientific reasons as to why change is difficult, and why your brain wiring will resist it. Now we need to talk about some harsh, painful truths regarding the way we think and how most of us fear the unknown. Yes, we fear change because it will take us into strange territory. In fact, we are more likely to continue living our lives the way we are – even if we aren't comfortable, are stressed, and know that our lifestyle is making us physically and mentally sick – rather than try something new. We will likely put our mental energy toward finding reasons why we can't change and why we must continue on the same path, doing the same things, over and over again. We might even justify why happiness is ultimately not a realistic goal. We might tell ourselves that we should learn to be content with what we have. Many of us feel guilty for not feeling satisfied with all the good things we have in our lives. 'It could always be worse.' 'Look how lucky you are.' 'There are always people suffering much more than you.' Yes, of course, there are many people much more misfortunate than you, dear reader. Interestingly, research has shown that those living in basic, impoverished, and difficult situations seem to have better abilities to be happy and content compared with those living in a developed nation. But if you truly believed that you did not deserve more happiness then you would not have picked up this book. So let us own our intrinsic goal for happiness, excitement, and satisfaction and work toward it. Now, what we need to do is learn to embrace the unknown as an opportunity and an area of growth and personal development.

Dealing with the fear of losing yourself!

Just recently, I had an interesting coaching conversation with a client who is at a point in their life where they can feel change coming up – necessary and wanted change, which, nevertheless, is causing them to feel uncertain and insecure. They are suddenly dealing with fears about loss, abandonment, loneliness, and lack of support. These fears are not irrational, as certainly change brings all of that. However, they came as a bit of a surprise to my generally confident and assertive client, and to myself. During our last session, we were able to narrow the cause of fear down to a rudimentary fear of losing themselves as a person and having to change their known identity. After the conversation, I realized that I had previously experienced similar fears. I found myself questioning if I was remaining my authentic self throughout my own processes of change or if I was becoming a victim to some sort of imposter syndrome. It is easy to get caught up in the vision of becoming this self-aware, Zen-like, determined, willful, and happy individual, but how can we make sure that this is truly who we are meant to be?

I think that, even when we are changing our mindsets and adopting new governing paradigms and beliefs, we do essentially remain who we are. It is rare for anyone to completely change their values, their core beliefs about the world, and their spiritual thoughts. We develop and adapt based on our circumstances, we learn and we grow based on experiences, and while we might be perceived differently by others, who we fundamentally are remains more or less unchanged. It is less about changing who we are and more about creating a change in our thoughts, emotions, and our subsequent behaviors.

As you are approaching these kinds of changes, however, it is absolutely expected to move through unknown, fearful emotions. It will be important for your success to deal with these feelings, to name them and explore them, and even to allow yourself to sit with them for a little while. Fears and doubts that are brushed under the carpet have the nasty habit of growing and multiplying until we can no longer ignore them.

☞ Exercise:

There are many more exercises on goal setting and paradigm shifts coming your way but let us finish this chapter with a few writing prompts. **Remember, no skipping exercises!**

Take pen and paper and answer the following questions as spontaneously as possible:

- When am I the happiest?
- What is holding me back from feeling like this more often?
- How can I introduce this feeling into other activities?
- What am I afraid of?
- What is the worst thing that could happen if I change the way I do things?

- How can I practice thinking outside of my comfort zone (this can be an activity, doing something differently, having a conversation with someone that challenges you, etc.)?

No, hold on! Did you do it?

What was your biggest takeaway from this chapter?

✳ Key points:

✳ Why is change so uncomfortable – the instinct of staying the same: We're creatures of habit, as the known feels safer than the unknown. Our brains are designed to form pathways that can be easily reused, to filter our experiences. We have a natural tendency to want to repeat ourselves in ways that we know are safe and proven to work.

✳ Exercising our change muscle: Acknowledge what you are currently doing/thinking, assess whether this will lead you to your goals, decide what will, and do it!

✳ Commit: Like any other exercise, it can be uncomfortable and difficult at times, but if we keep showing up and putting ourselves in the practices, we'll continue to grow in our ability to change.

✳ Fear of losing ourselves: Even through changing our mindsets and adopting new governing paradigms and beliefs, I do feel we essentially remain who we are.

The focus is on creating a change in our thoughts, emotions, and our subsequent behaviors so we can elect what serves us best.

Our thoughts create our reality!

With the increasing interest and demand for mental health interventions and treatment methods, there have been a wide range of sciences emerging that aim to investigate how we can lead healthier and happier lives. Some life coaching methodologies, which I personally find particularly interesting, aim to combine the findings of Quantum Physics with neuroscience and behavioral psychology. Quantum physics is the study of energy and matter at the most fundamental level, and according to its theories, our thoughts are the source of our reality. Wherever we direct our thought energy is where we create emotions and, in turn, produce our life experiences. Given that no two brains are alike, our individual, internal perceptions and realities are different, even if we might share the same experiences and situations with other people. This also means that we can change, influence, and affect our view of events, and that we are effectively in control.

The suggestion of taking ownership and responsibility for events that we find ourselves in, especially if they are negative, might sound radical at first. It is understandable if you are initially not comfortable with this statement, as many aren't. It can appear as if we are blaming the victim. Obviously, nobody wants to create a horrible reality for themselves in which they are abused, sick, poor, or suffering.

However, from my personal experience helping individuals change their thinking and behavior for over 15 years, I do have to agree that we are indeed creating much of our own emotional experience and reality by the way we think about a situation. Getting stuck in a negative, hopeless mindset is easy, and it doesn't help that many society constructs tell us that hardship and suffering is normal and should be endured. Fortunately, times are changing, and we are more likely than ever before to accept our responsibility in the creation of our circumstances.

Our bodies and minds have the power to constantly change, alter, and create. At any given moment, you could theoretically create a completely different experience for yourself, just through the power of thought. It is no coincidence that my business is called 'Created Coaching'. So let us no longer deny our power and own it proudly!

Throughout our lives, we are confronted with three types of experiences, situations, and events: the ones over which we have no control, the ones we can influence to some extent, and the ones we can fully control.

The many situations we are exposed to and have no control over include circumstances such as the family and location we were born into, accidents of all kinds, incidents such as pandemics and job layoffs, death of loved ones, illnesses, and so on. These are experiences that we go through and are aware of.

Situations that we can influence are interactive events. We can greatly impact other living beings with our interactions.

If we walked up to a stranger in a supermarket and started verbally abusing them, then that person would most probably react differently than if we had smiled and politely asked where we could find the butter. However, we do not control how that person responds to our offensive behavior. They might decide to shout back, ignore us, walk away, or do something completely different. We cannot even predict how a person responds to friendly behavior. I am sure we all have had interactions with others who seem to be stuck in their own unhappiness, appear unwarrantedly rude, impolite, and treat us in a way we don't think we deserve, despite us putting a friendly foot forward.

Events that we fully control are the decisions that we take to alter the course of a situation. Having a cup of coffee in the morning, or not, is such a free decision. Every day, we make many of these decisions that are theoretically completely under our own power. However, we often find reasons to believe that we are restricted by our circumstances. Whether our situation is really holding us back or not is not as important as recognizing that it is our thoughts about it that matter. If you are completely unhappy in your job but choose to stay in the position because you are afraid of not being able to provide for your family, finding another job, etc. – this is a free choice. You have chosen to let your fear make the decision. Yet theoretically, the two options of quitting or staying in your current job are both available to you.

Our power, and this is where we can shape, influence, and define our reality, is that we can control how we perceive, interpret, and think about the events in our life. In turn, these thoughts create an emotional experience, which will subsequently define our behavior and responses to these events. No one else can choose our thoughts and actions; they are ours if we claim them.

I often tell my clients my train analogy. Imagine our thoughts as trains. The more we engage with any thought, the more we fuel the train. The emotional connection to that thought is what can really speed the train up and get it to move faster and faster. But as with real trains, our thought trains travel on rails and have a certain destination, the final station. We need to decide wisely and carefully which train we board and be certain that we want to reach its destination. In other words, we need to be sure that we engage with thoughts that will lead to our desired outcome. If we think negative thoughts and give a lot of energy to them, then we shouldn't be surprised if our emotional experience is not a happy one.

One important detail that we need to acknowledge is that **emotions are not facts**. Unfortunately, rather than assessing our actual circumstances and reality, we often get stuck running on autopilot. As we continue to tell ourselves and others the same stories about our lives, our pasts, our struggles, our miseries, and our reasons for all of them, we subconsciously repeat the same emotional experience over and over again. When this happens, we let our emotions run our lives.

Our emotions are internal experiences that are a reaction to something that happens externally, mixed up with lingering emotions from past experiences. In an ideal scenario, we should learn how to cope with triggering emotions during our upbringing. If you observe consciously, you can probably notice some shared patterns in how your family members deal with stressful emotions themselves. If those who raised you do not possess mature coping techniques, you might not have been able to develop your own. When our emotions control our life experience, then we often operate in survival mode, which hinders our ability to logically assess a situation.

Imagine you are suddenly laid off from work and your immediate thoughts are, 'I messed up. They fired me because I wasn't good enough. I will never find work again. I am useless.' You will likely go through severely negative emotions such as low self-esteem, self-hatred, desperation, and even depression, and you will likely engage in activities that align with these feelings, such as staying in bed and not being motivated. Even if you manage to send out a few job applications and even secure an interview – imagine how difficult it might be to show up with a positive attitude and create a good first impression. It can easily become a vicious cycle of feeling low and creating more low moments. But now imagine what would have happened if your first thought had been that you are so glad to be rid of this boring job and finally have a chance to find something that you will enjoy and can excel at. Suddenly your emotional experience, and in turn your actions, become completely different. We choose which thought we think.

This was a superficial example, and our abilities as creators are much more detailed and sensitive. If we think a thought repeatedly, give it energy and truth, it will become a belief. Our beliefs create a cognitive filter through which we interpret all events in our life. We then use this filter to select evidence that matches up with what we already believe to be true. These beliefs are our paradigms, which, over time, become deeply embedded in our subconscious mind. Remember the psychological term 'cognitive bias' that was described in the chapter, 'Why is change so difficult?'

Example:

One of my clients has been through a difficult divorce. She is a successful VP and used to represent her company publicly. Throughout the divorce proceedings, she discovered that she was cheated on, and her soon-to-be ex-husband gave her strong reason to assume that he did not find her attractive any longer, which, so he argued, led him to go astray and was the reason the marriage was falling apart. During the divorce process, my client formed a strong belief that she was not desirable, despite being celebrated as a beautiful, successful, and a powerful woman in business prior to this event. In one of our sessions, she obsessed over a comment someone made about her appearance during an event. That person thought her dress was interesting. She had been struggling with this comment for a few days when we finally met, and she was unable to think about anything else. In fact, she engaged in destructive self-talk, even calling herself stupid for believing she could have pulled the colorful dress off. It was only after I made her recall all the positive comments about her appearance that she had received at the same event that she realized that she had completely ignored the positive, which in numbers far outweighed the one, not even severely negative, comment. She had chosen her reality and filtered events to find the one that aligned with her belief: that she is not attractive.

Our beliefs and paradigms are, of course, often formed from early childhood and are a mix of our cultural environment, the beliefs of our parents and family, our early life experiences, and the statements we hear frequently. They are also influenced by the experiences we witness others going through, and the way others deal with those events. But as in the example above, beliefs can also develop in adulthood and can even be contrary to previous paradigms.

Our beliefs become our self-concept, they become who we are ('I am' beliefs), and what we are capable of ('I can' beliefs). From this self-concept, we create stories, statements, and narratives that we tell ourselves and others about who we are and what we can and cannot do.

Some common negative paradigms include:

'I am not good enough.'
'I don't deserve this.'
'I have to be perfect.'
'I am an imposter.'
'I am not lovable.'

Some, unfortunately, not-so-common positive paradigms include:

'I deserve this.'
'I am smart.'
'I am capable.'
'I can achieve my goals.'
'I am loved.'

We are the main characters in our story, and we subconsciously write the script based on our self-created self-beliefs.

☞ Exercise:

Think of an event that recently triggered an emotional reaction in you. It does not matter if the reaction was positive or negative. Using the paradigms listed above, create different outcomes for your event by imagining you would have these different beliefs.

How would the emotional response and subsequent reaction have changed with these different beliefs?

Maybe you can already recognize one of your core paradigms that you used in your specific event, but we will come back to this later.

In our heads, we develop hypothetical expectations about the outcome of an event based on what we believe to be likely and/or possible. We then act in a way that is consistent with these expectations. Often, we will act on our anticipations before an event happens, and through that, we can create a certain experience. This is what is called the 'self-fulfilling prophecy'. Because we are sure of the outcome of a situation, we act in a way that will enable that said outcome to become a reality. This participation in forming our reality happens whether we are aware of it or not.

There is nothing magical about it; however, quantum physics has more refined explanations based on our energetic fields. If you are interested in reading more, then I highly recommend that you familiarize yourself with the work of Dr Joe Dispenza, a neuroscientist and author who is teaching about the empowerment of the mind.

As we've discussed earlier in this book, naturally, and unfortunately, we will always encounter situations that are completely outside of our control. There will be hardship, sorrow, illness, and unhappiness as part of our human existence. But as the intelligent and sensible beings that we are, we do have control over how we think and feel, and subsequently, we control what these uncontrollable events do to us and how they affect our lives. This is our intrinsic human gift and the key to how we can create our own experience. Have you realized that there are always people that thrive and grow in times of crisis? It is not because they are lucky; more likely, they chose to see opportunity rather than misfortune.

As we have discussed in the previous chapter, it is not easy to break out of our autopilot and master a mindset shift toward a more conscious and aware way of thinking. Thought and mindset control is an art that requires practice, focus and dedication. The more difficult our lives have been, the more stuck we might find ourselves in our negative paradigms. But fortunately, like with anything else in life, we can start with small, doable steps, and the more we practice, the better we get at it. This is your life, and you are now aware of the intense power you hold over creating it. You owe it to yourself to at least try making an impactful change.

**'Whether you think you can or think you can't,
you are right.'**

– Henry Ford

✶ Key points:

- ✶ Make sure you are on the right train: Our thoughts are like trains. As with real trains, our thought trains travel on rails and have a specific destination. We need to decide wisely and carefully which train we board and be certain that we want to reach its final stop! We need to be sure that we engage with thoughts that will lead to our desired outcome.

- ✶ Shaping our reality filter: Our beliefs create our reality. How we think and speak about ourselves and the outer world becomes our way of interacting. These narratives we tell ourselves ('I'm not smart', 'I'm funny', etc.) are foundational to our being. We need to identify the stories we tell ourselves so we can assess which ones serve us and which ones don't.

- ✶ One event, many outcomes – practicing with different filters: To help us identify suitable filters, we can look at an event (either a personal experience or a hypothetical event) and practice viewing the outcomes of that moment through different governing beliefs (even if these beliefs aren't ours, we can practice changing the nature of the selected event through the filter of the new belief).

Creating a paradigm shift

By now you are hopefully quite eager to know how we can create paradigm shifts and how we can use this concept to our advantage to create happier, more satisfying lifestyles. But before we dive into it, let us just take some time to make sure that we really understand the importance of our paradigms.

When I use the phrase 'paradigm' in this book, I talk about our own individual constructs and beliefs. As I mentioned previously, we can imagine them like a lens through which we see the world, and they are responsible for our reactions to events and situations. In science, however, a paradigm is traditionally defined as the basic assumptions, ways of thinking, and research methods that are accepted by a discipline or wider group. If it is more intuitive to you, you can always stick to the word 'belief', and I will also use 'paradigm' and 'belief' interchangeably.

Now, let us investigate the reason our paradigms have so much power and influence over our subconscious actions.

Did you know that our subconscious mind holds around 90% of the brain's processing ability? It is a huge memory bank, which permanently stores information about everything that happens to us and has virtually unlimited capacity. Therefore, taking regular stock of what is going on in our subconscious mind is paramount to living a conscious life. Imagine your subconscious mind like a massive processing computer with executive function. Our paradigms are the coded instructions that tell the computer what to do, and the computer then sends the message to the rest of our system. As with any automated function, we need to rewrite the commands based on our current situation and desired outcome; however, what often happens is that the coding remains the same for most of our lives, even though the programs might originate in our early childhood. That's not very smart, is it?

How do our paradigms develop?

In the chapter, 'Our thoughts create our reality', I gave the example of my successful, and very beautiful client, who, as the result of an ugly divorce, developed a new paradigm: 'I am not attractive.' This is an example of a sudden onset belief that resulted from a traumatic experience in adulthood. Prior to this event, my client was a rather confident and self-assured woman. Because the paradigm was recently acquired, and not well established, my client was able to reject it and quickly replace it with a more beneficial mindset. She was able to restore her positive self-image. However, would she not have taken immediate action and course correction, her new belief could have easily become strongly ingrained in her brain and continued to affect all her relationships and interactions, be they personal or professional. Off of this, consider that most of our strong self-beliefs that govern our subconscious actions do start to form and develop earlier on in life; it's no wonder we can have trouble rewriting them. All the same, it is doable.

The brain is really fascinating! With research constantly advancing and new findings from neuroscience and neuropsychology emerging, we have become more aware of how little we still understand the complexity and abilities of this organ. We now know that the brain is constantly changing and adapting based on our experiences. This is called neuroplasticity. This umbrella term describes the brain's ability to reorganize itself and grow new neural networks and pathways no matter our age. Neuroplasticity leads to both structural and functional changes. Our brains are composed of around 110 billion neurons. In early neuroscientific research, it was believed that neurogenesis, the formation of new neurons, ended shortly after birth; however, we now understand that neuroplasticity allows the brain to reorganize pathways, create new connections, and can even create new neurons throughout our lives.

Functional plasticity describes the brain's ability to bypass damaged areas of the brain and move functions to a different, healthy part. Structural plasticity is the ability to change the physical structure because of learning, experience, and development. Every time you acquire new information, be it by reading, hearing about it, or experiencing it, your brain might undergo structural changes. That is if you decide to mentally engage with that new information and put your thought energy toward it (remember the train analogy).

Understanding neuroplasticity

In our early childhood, our brains undergo rapid growth. Our young brain forms more than a million neural connections every second! When we are born, every neuron in our cerebral cortex has around 2500 synapses. These are small gaps between the neurons, where nerve impulses are relayed. This number will have increased to around 15000 synapses per neuron by the time we are age three. However, as adults, we only have about half that number. Synaptic pruning is responsible for that, a process whereby some connections are strengthened and others are eliminated based on our experiences. The neurons that we frequently need develop stronger connections, but the ones that are never, or just rarely, used will eventually die. The brain will, however, develop new connections, as it adapts to changing environments.

Neuroplasticity enables our brain to learn new things and enhance our cognitive abilities, but also allows us to recover from traumatic brain injuries and strokes and to regain function where it has declined. But more importantly, we can use our understanding of the brain's adaptive abilities and the resulting possibility to change our emotional responses and behavior to our advantage.

Plasticity occurs throughout all our life; however, certain changes are more predominant at specific ages. Because younger brains are so rapidly developing and organizing themselves, they are much more sensitive and responsive to experiences. However, this does not mean that an older brain cannot adapt. It simply means that the neurological pathways have been strengthened over time and might be more resistant to change.

You can't teach an old dog new tricks?

Whilst this was believed to be true in the past, research has revealed that the brain will continue to change in response to learning, no matter what age. In fact, learning has not only been found to be possible but also beneficial for the elderly, as it continues to stimulate greater neuron recruitment and connectivity within the brain. This positively affects memory, attention, thinking and reasoning skills, and can even help to reduce the risk of dementia. However, the brain's malleability does have limitations. Certain actions, such as movement, language, speech, and cognition are mostly generated and controlled by certain brain areas. If these key areas are damaged, some recovery may be possible; however, deficits will likely occur, as other areas of the brain cannot fully cover those functions.

How can we improve our brain's neuroplasticity?

There are many ways we can stimulate neuroplasticity and gain the many benefits that go beyond achieving paradigm shifts more smoothly. Exposing ourselves to environments that promote learning, novelty, and food for thought all stimulate positive changes. Whilst we naturally encourage our children to learn, discover, have hobbies, and try new things, we tend to not treat ourselves to the same enriching activities as we grow older and let our busy work schedules dictate our daily lives.

So why not include one of the following to your 3-month bucket list (see also the chapter '3-month bucket list'):

• Learn a new language.
• Travel and explore new places.

- Learn how to play an instrument.
- Become an expert on a topic of choice.
- Read books on different topics.
- Paint or engage in creative activities.
- Learn or try a new sport or activity.

The importance of exercise and rest in neuroplasticity

As with any kind of change, whether physical or mental in nature, we need to appreciate that growth is a result of adaptation to new situations and challenges. Being exposed to these new environments, as well as the actual act of growing, exposes the body to stress on a cellular level. Further, growth does not actually happen whilst we are undergoing the stimulus, but rather when we are resting. This is when the body, or the brain, has the capacity to build new tissue, connections, and neurological pathways.

Research has verified that the quality and quantity of sleep greatly impact dendrites, the new growth at the end of neurons. It has further been found that sleep deprivation disrupts both structural and functional brain functions, as well as grey matter volume.[*]

In addition to rest and sleep, regular physical exercise also has a range of benefits not only for the body but also

---

[*] Long Z, Cheng F, Lei X. Age effect on gray matter volume changes after sleep restriction. PLoS One. 2020 Feb 6;15(2):e0228473. doi: 10.1371/journal.pone.0228473. Erratum in: PLoS One. 2021 Feb 4;16(2):e0246799. PMID: 32027695; PMCID: PMC7004551.

the brain. Studies indicate that exercise may decrease the risk for neuron loss in key areas of the hippocampus, the region of the brain involved in memory, alongside other functions. Additionally, physical activity seems to play a role in new neuron formation, also in the hippocampus. A study that investigated the positive effect of exercise on brain plasticity through its impact on the brain-derived neurotrophic factor – a protein that impacts nerve growth and functional connectivity – found that this appears to happen even beyond the time of the exercise intervention, for up to one week.[*]

Brain changes are mostly positive events and enable growth on many psychological and physiological levels; however, they can also signify negative change when there are detrimental changes to the structure and function caused by disease, brain injury, or even traumatic events, resulting in post-traumatic stress disorder.

The organizing ability of our brain

We talked about how the brain connects new input and new experiences to existing thoughts. But why does it need to do this?

Imagine all the thoughts about the things we need to do, such as daily activities (walking, talking, movement, etc.), as well as

---

[*] Guendalina Bastioli, Jennifer C. Arnold, Maria Mancini, Adam C. Mar, Begoña Gamallo-Lana, Khalil Saadipour, Moses V. Chao, Margaret E. Rice. Voluntary Exercise Boosts Striatal Dopamine Release: Evidence for the Necessary and Sufficient Role of BDNF. Journal of Neuroscience 8 June 2022, 42 (23) 4725-4736; **DOI:** 10.1523/JNEUROSCI.2273-21.2022

all the incoming information that needs to be processed and potentially reacted to (sensory information, new learnings, etc.). All these thoughts are swirling around in the mind, and the brain needs to be able to move from one thought to the next in an organized, timely, and orderly manner. Our mind is always active and busy perceiving, processing, organizing, planning, and remembering. However, we don't even notice most of our brain's activity as we follow our daily routines. To be able to keep up with this immense task of staying on top of all the incoming information as well as maintaining usual daily functions, the brain integrates information and has developed a filing system.

Our nervous system can handle endless streams of incoming data. Our senses are the interface between our brain and our external environment. They receive stimuli and translate them into nerve signals that are articulated to the brain. Here, the information gets processed and uses relevant information to create thoughts, which we can either verbally express or the mind can store them for future use. However, the brain does not just gather information from external environments; it constantly adds input from emotions and memory. Hence, emotional experiences and memories are powerful influences on our thoughts and behaviors. Our cognitive abilities are exceptionally complex. But whilst cognition is an essential feature of our consciousness, we do not experience most of its aspects consciously!

In cognitive psychology, there are detailed models explaining the organization of information, and some interesting concepts are being investigated; a lot of our brains' marvelous abilities are yet to be discovered. What is important for us is to understand that we need to bring our paradigms into our conscious mind to be able to work with them, and to ensure that they are still relevant to our current situation, needs, and desires.

Our mind might sometimes, accidentally, overwrite the real facts by jumping to conclusions based on our emotional experiences (of the past) and our paradigms. Of course, our brains are extremely smart and always try to be as effective and efficient as possible. Imagine if we had to think and actively control every single thought and every single movement. Brushing our teeth for example. We would have to think about raising our hands, grabbing the toothbrush and toothpaste, opening the toothpaste, deciding how much we want on the toothbrush, squeezing it on, opening the faucet…. All the many, many movements and decisions that together create the 'toothbrushing activity'. By the way, what did it feel like to brush your teeth this morning? How was the taste of your toothpaste? As you're reading this, you might wonder if you did, in fact, brush your teeth this morning. Don't worry, that is perfectly normal, given that this task is firmly embedded in your subconscious mind!

You get the idea; it would be extremely time-consuming and slow if our daily tasks and actions had to be controlled and led consciously. Hence all the repetitive tasks (I am talking about physical actions now) are firmly stored as sequences in our subconscious mind.

The same accounts for walking, eating, drinking, and getting dressed in the morning – all the habitual tasks that we do every day, even driving a car. Did you ever find yourself mentally drifting off while driving? Or taking an exit that you often take, even though you were planning to drive somewhere completely different? It can be dangerous if we are so habitual in the act of driving that we don't give full attention to the road anymore simply because we've driven the same road repeatedly. That is a good example of how, sometimes, this great ability of our mind to automate actions can be harmful, or at least increase risk.

This process is similar to our emotional responses and our reactions to situations. Instead of having to analyze and question events every time, we develop an automated, immediate response to the interactions that we experience often and are exposed to frequently. We form our opinion, our belief, and store it in our subconscious mind. Surely you can recall a situation when you 'snapped', when something triggered you and you immediately responded, maybe in a heightened emotional manner. Do you remember the amygdala hijack? It may have been one of those, or it might have been that your paradigm got attacked and you got triggered. Most probably it was a mix of both. In these kinds of situations, we do not take the time to consciously analyze how we want to, and should, react. We simply burst out with our response before we even know it. Whether you prefer the physiological (amygdala hijack), or the psychological explanation (trigger), your subconscious has taken over control.

Let me give you an example of one of my clients, which some of you might identify with. This client, let us call her

Karma, has two young daughters, a stressful job reporting to one of the most senior executives in her company, and a husband. She also has three siblings, and her mother lives close by. From an early age, Karma was the responsible one in the family; she always received a lot of praise for being the 'good girl', the one everybody could depend on. She really enjoyed the role of the caretaker and took a lot of pride in it. Whilst her parents didn't overload her with any age-inappropriate tasks, she knew that she was of great help to them and developed a special bond with her late father.

When Karma started her working career, she maintained her helpful attitude, making sure to look out for her co-workers and diligently completing tasks as quickly and accurately as possible. Very soon, she was recognized by her superiors for being dependable, fast, and always willing to take on more work. Karma just never said 'no'. I clearly remember Karma's response to my initial assessment question about her desired outcome for our sessions. She said, 'I cannot do this anymore. When is it ever going to stop?' My response: Whenever you tell it to stop. In addition to her extremely demanding work schedule, which often required her to stay in the office until 7 or 8 pm, she also had her two daughters that she didn't spend enough time with. Her youngest sister was going through a rough time, and Karma spent many hours on the phone, having unfruitful conversations that were mentally draining. She felt burned out, drained, and hopeless. There was no joy in Karma's life, and she felt overwhelmed by her responsibilities. It seemed like life was an ongoing, huge mountain of chores, tasks, and duties that were about to bury her alive.

We followed the steps listed below to identify her paradigms and, very quickly, the most debilitating one became apparent: 'I am responsible for everything.' This came with a little sidekick of, 'I must never say "no".' Again, you will find an exercise below to guide you through your own scenario.

Karma decided that she no longer needed these paradigms. She understood that they came from a time when she was young and influenced by the great feelings of appreciation and love she received from her parents. Her adult self was able to rationalize that she was not loved BECAUSE she was the responsible one, but her young brain had, a long time ago, made that connection. She just kept living her life with these paradigms, expecting to get the same good feelings from her actions. However, she came to the realization that this was no longer the case. In fact, her inability to say 'no' led her to overload her plate and was a great source of stress and unhappiness, not only for herself but also for her husband and kids.

Karma decided to try on some new paradigm, 'I am responsible for myself' and 'I can choose to support others to help themselves'. These new paradigms helped her to have an important talk with her sister, telling her that she could no longer listen to her complaints for hours, but would be very happy to have a productive chat to support her in developing a solution-focused action plan. To her surprise, her sister told her that their other siblings and even their mother had long ago stopped listening to her pour her heart out in the way she had been with Karma, demanding that she'd act. By continuing to listen to her, Karma had accidentally enabled her sister's misery.

Karma decided to leave work at 5 pm, every day, to spend time with her daughters. At first, this was a great cause of anxiety for her and felt like an impossible thing to do. Initially, she asked me, 'How can I just leave? What do I say?' She looked at me puzzled when I told her to use her legs, and simply make her way out of the building. However, having decided that she was responsible only for herself, she managed and learned that a lot of her colleagues were leaving at sensible times too. Miraculously, her workload seemed to be half, and she was able to finish everything on time whilst maintaining the high quality of her work. A big contributing factor was that she no longer took on tasks that were not really hers, but rather assisted others in figuring out the best ways to do it. She told me that, a few weeks after she made these changes, a younger colleague told her that he really appreciated that he was able to learn from her; he felt she was finally trusting him to accomplish tasks. He had previously disliked that Karma wouldn't let him try and was feeling quite useless and inadequate. Her biggest win was when one of her superiors told her that she had always been a great asset to the company, but finally acted like a leader. Overall, the impact of changing her paradigms made a huge difference in Karma's personal and professional life, as it will in yours.

Creating your paradigm shift

Now it is time for the good news: YOU can take back control too! Once we gain awareness and become conscious of our subconscious patterns and paradigms, we can make informed decisions. It is estimated that most of us have three to five main paradigms that greatly influence our everyday actions, emotions, and overall life.

The two following exercises are extremely powerful tools that you can use again and again, as much as needed. In fact, I do recommend that you do them at least every six months, to make sure your paradigms are still aligned with your desired outcome and the direction you wish to take for your life.

In the beginning, and this also applies if you're not fully decided on your goals just yet (more in the chapter 'Emotional Connection to Goals'), you will most likely try on a few new paradigms for fit and comfort. Play with it and enjoy the process!

☞ **Exercise:**

Identify one of your paradigms.

Steps:

- Think about a situation that triggered you.
- What about this situation triggered you?
- What was the emotional reaction?
- What is your core belief that was triggered?

Example:

- *My boss treated me unjustly in front of my colleagues!*
- *Being exposed.*

- *I felt humiliated and ashamed.*
- *I can never let my guard down!*

Well done! Now that you have identified one of your paradigms, you get to decide what you want to do with it.

You may decide to keep it, and that is perfectly ok. If your paradigm is still needed and supports you on your journey toward your desired, happy outcome, you should.

You might decide to modify it, maybe soften it a little, take the edge off.

Or you might decide that it is no longer useful and to replace it with something new. This new paradigm does not always have to be opposite to the old one. It can be something completely different that reflects your desired mindset.

Remember, this is completely your story to write!

Assessing your paradigms

Steps:

- Decide if you want to keep, modify, or change your paradigm.
- Decide on a new paradigm, if applicable.
- Play through the situation in your head with the new paradigm – what is the changed outcome?

Example:

- *I want to modify the paradigm.*
- *Instead of 'I can never let my guard down', I'll go with, 'I am trying to understand the context before assuming bad intentions'.*
- *I can see that I might not have produced the best possible work. I don't like the way the critique was presented and will communicate that professionally with my boss.*

Creating your paradigm shift is simple, but it is not necessarily easy!

I use the above exercises with every single one of my clients. They never fail to produce great results, and most of my clients are surprised by how quickly they can switch to their new belief. However, the timeline of the process is different for everyone. Initially, it might take you a few days to even realize that you used your old paradigm in a situation. This is perfectly fine. All you have to do is play out in your mind how this situation would have been different had you used your new paradigm. How you would have acted and how you would have felt. I recommend taking some time every evening and reflecting on the events of the day. This can help you to analyze events that were controlled by your old paradigms. Very soon, the time between the event and your realization will shorten, and you will eventually be able to use your new paradigm right there, when the situation occurs.

Please be patient with yourself and trust the process. We are not actually overwriting the old brain wirings; we are creating new ones. The more often we use them, the stronger these new connections get. The old ones will get weaker and eventually disappear (you can re-read about this above in the section on 'plasticity'). Therefore, imagining the event as if you had used your new paradigm is the most important and powerful part of the process.

You might wonder if we need to keep our new paradigms in the conscious mind, and the answer is no. Once you are satisfied with your paradigm you can happily let your mind go back to what it does so well: automate processes. But remember, we should frequently assess what is happening in our subconscious mind and course-correct if needed. This is the most impactful tool to create a conscious, happy, fulfilling life. I know you will very soon experience dramatic changes and align your reality with your desires and dreams.

✶ Key points:

- ✶ What is a paradigm: A paradigm is like a lens through which we see the world; they are responsible for our reactions to events and situations.
- ✶ The subconscious filing system: We are constantly faced with a large volume of incoming information. The brain deals with all this information by organizing common themes in ways that make it easier to categorize as it comes in. This is a useful tool, but can sometimes be detrimental when the filing system is based on something that no longer serves us.

* Bringing the paradigm out into the conscious mind: These filing patterns/paradigms – the stories we tell ourselves – are often unconscious. With practice, we can bring these stories into the conscious mind. From here, we can choose which we keep and which we let go.

* Remember: It's a process of slow, gentle, elimination. It's just a matter of continuing on with the newly chosen paradigm. It might feel awkward at first, but eventually, we'll get used to it and adopt it. The old paradigm will, sooner or later, weaken and fall away.

Creating pockets of happiness

Science has proven that we humans are naturally more on the pessimistic side. We tend to expect negative outcomes, be cautious, and always be prepared for possible dangers to make themselves known. Our brains are wired to scan our surroundings for potential risks and remember them for the future. You might find that if you think back to your last few days, or weeks, you might be naturally focusing on the things that went wrong rather than all the events that turned out well, or even better than expected.

This mental hardwiring stems, of course, from our long-gone ancestors, who needed this trait for survival. When you are constantly having to prepare for life-threatening situations, you certainly want to always be cautiously aware of the dangers around you, and, well, expect the worst. Life back then must have been extremely tough – and short-lived.

But in this time and age, how many of us are experiencing these kinds of disasters on a daily basis? Regardless, many of us still sense, feel, act, and think as if we are. Our brains are still programmed to be cautious, even though the world around us has changed dramatically and is a much safer place. This is important to realize because if we are not consciously aware of this intrinsic way of thinking, then we are merely a victim to it and can easily find ourselves caught in negative, unrealistic, and fear-driven thought patterns.

Our cautious and conservative way of thinking even impacts the way we learn, develop our physical abilities, and study. Starting from childhood, we are taught to improve in the subjects and disciplines we are naturally not too good at, rather than focusing on what we are already excelling in. We learn to improve our shortcomings and often consider this more important than nurturing our strengths. In many cultures, we find excellence not to be a celebrated trait, but something that is stigmatized by the idea that standing out is a bad thing. It's safer to blend in and become invisible in the masses.

Even though this thought pattern is deeply ingrained, it is quite easily observed, brought into our conscious mind, and then replaced with a more favorable approach. This process, of course, requires some time and consistent practice.

A coaching tool that teaches you awareness of unnecessary negativity is 'Reality Testing' – initially put forward by Sigmund Freud. With this technique, we assess the validity of a thought and evaluate it logically, rather than emotionally. Reality Testing is an exercise that can be useful in a wide variety of situations and contexts.

All our thoughts are constantly influenced by our feelings. As we have already learned, our brain cannot differentiate between emotional responses to a past event and a current situation – it will treat them as one. Merely thinking about a triggering situation will cause the same release of hormones as experiencing it. Therefore, Reality Testing is a life skill, rather than a coaching skill, and should become a habitual part of your self-awareness toolbox. This exercise will enable you to judge situations appropriately and improve your reactions to situations. But most importantly, you will notice your emotional response and might be able to analyze where this feeling comes from.

Example – 'I failed my first exam of the year. I am going to fail the rest of my exams as well.'

Reality – Failing at something initially does not equate to a pattern of failure and does not mean that things can't improve or change in the future.

Emotions – Possibly not confident in own abilities, low self-esteem, self-undermining thought pattern.

Remember that our brain landscape is moldable but will be reinforced in its old beliefs whenever we think a thought or feel an emotion that leads to a thought. In fact, our brain cannot differentiate between emotions that belong to the past and emotional responses to a current event. This means whenever we feel a negative emotion, such as anger, disappointment, fear, loneliness, resentment, self-hatred, etc., as an emotional response to a memory, it is the same as if this response was to a current event. To make matters worse, our emotional response to an actual situation in the present moment is going to be intensified if there are similar previous situations that are anchored in our subconscious mind!

Reintroducing Happiness

To snap our brain out of its habitual pessimism and the resulting negative wiring, it is important to create what I like to call 'pockets of happiness'. Initially, these little happy moments can be short, but we will aim to have several happy pockets each day. The smallest happy thought will help your brain to remember how to produce those happy hormones we have been talking about, and you will begin to remember what happy feels like. As simple as this exercise might sound, it is impactful, especially if you've spent a prolonged period of time feeling stressed, unhappy, or overwhelmed.

Short mindfulness exercises can be a good starting point, e.g., consciously listening to your favorite song; admiring the beauty of a flower; watching a child play, or even joining in on the game; smelling your favorite perfume; having loving, caring thoughts about a special person; practicing appreciation; mindful breathing; savoring the taste of a drink or meal; etc. The list is endless! What is important is that you allow yourself to be fully present and engaged in the activity and really feel it and the happiness that comes with it.

But before we practice, let's go one step back. We all want to be happy, right? Given that this could be considered a universal goal, it is astounding how little time we spend defining our 'happy'. We all need different emotions, feelings, sensations, and situations to feel content, joyful, and in the flow. What excites one person might be annoying to another. You will easily find examples within your family or group of friends. In fact, we often know better what makes other people happy than ourselves. Yet, we all have our own individual happiness formula, which we need to find.

At the end of this chapter, you'll find a questionnaire that helps you start thinking about your drivers, motivators, and your own unique happiness formula. I suggest that you revisit this exercise often and continue to fine-tune your formula. What makes you happy will most probably change over time, and it's important to always stay intentionally connected to this process.

Once you gain more clarity about what makes you happy, you can connect your short pockets of happiness into more long-lasting intervals and be able to experience happiness much more frequently and in a broader variety of settings and situations.

Science now believes that the frequency, and not the intensity, of happiness is what is important for our overall well-being. That means that we do not always need to be euphorically happy. In fact, it has been found that individuals who experience occasional times of great euphoria are overall less happy than those who are consistently or frequently living in a state of contentment and satisfaction. The tiny happy moments that you actively create and enjoy will soon have a big impact on your overall well-being.[*]

It can be quite a sensitive and triggering process to take yourself out of your usual state of unhappiness, whether that means stress, depression, anxiety, fear, or a simple fight-or-flight response. As we discussed in the previous chapters on the brain and stress, we are only ever using one nervous system, either in a sympathetic or parasympathetic state. Once we spend most of our time in one of these two, our brain and body get used to the hormones that go with it. As we've discussed, we can even get addicted to stress hormones, such as cortisol and adrenaline, which can lead to reckless or self-destructive behavior and an inability to feel satisfied if these hormone levels are low. If you are experiencing strong adverse reactions, mental and/ or physical discomfort – or any other strong reactions to practicing the pockets of happiness – you might want to seek assistance from a professional. However, also note that this often is a challenging process and that your brain might try to sabotage and resist the change. Take it easy, don't rush, and celebrate even the smallest success. Your brain will soon be able to recognize and enjoy the new happiness hormones.

---

[*]   Diener, E., Napa Scollon, C., & Lucas, R. E. (2009). The evolving concept of subjective well-being: The multifaceted nature of happiness. *Assessing well-being: The collected works of Ed Diener*, 67-100.

Our neurotransmitter and hormone balance can restore a more beneficial balance for overall health and well-being when we move away from experiencing stress and move toward experiencing gratitude, love, happiness, and joy.

But as mentioned before, if we are constantly on the edge, expecting the worst, dwelling in our ancestor's pessimism, and reliving traumatic experiences, then we are simply modulating our brain to be unbalanced and unhappy. The body will release more stress hormones and we find ourselves in a vicious cycle. Creating pockets of happiness is the easiest way to disrupt the ongoing stream of negative cascades.

You will immediately benefit from this exercise by allowing your brain to create new wirings, even if there is initial resistance. You will enable a reset of your system and decrease the impact of stress, anxiety, and negative thought patterns and teach yourself to be present, mindful, conscious and, well, happy! If we re-learn to be content and present, we can feel happier. Don't worry if you are feeling numb or if you forgot what it feels like to be happy. Just trust the process and start small – with contentment!

☞ **Exercise:**

Creating pockets of Happiness

Make a list of small activities and things that make you feel happy, relaxed, and content, e.g., listening to music, sitting in the garden, etc. Ideally, these should be activities that take around 5–15 minutes and don't require much preparation.

1.

2.

3.

4.

5.

6.

7.

8.

9.

10.

How can you integrate the above into your daily routine? Note down at least three pockets of happiness that you can do every day and commit to a specific time. Then put them into your diary and calendar. I also recommend setting an alarm on your phone.

Pocket #1:

Time:

Pocket #2:

Time:

Pocket #3:

☞ Exercise:

Defining your Happiness Formula

Use a sheet of paper or your journal to reflect on the following writing prompts:

I am the happiest when I ...

I am feeling relaxed and calm when ...

The last time I was completely happy was (describe the situation in detail) ...

What made me so happy in this situation was …

Things I need to be happy more often are …

✴ Key points:

- ✴ It's quantity, not quality: Rather than waiting for those rare moments of intense high and elation, it's important to get ourselves accustomed to regular and frequent small moments of happiness.

- ✴ The pocket practice: To snap our brain out of its habitual pessimism and the resulting negative wiring, it's important to create what I like to call, 'pockets of happiness'. It's the practice of having several happy pockets each day: consciously listening to your favorite song, admiring the beauty of a flower, etc.

- ✴ Remember: Happiness, like so many other things, is a practice. By practicing happiness, we are actively working on reshaping and rewiring our brains. It might feel difficult at first, but you will soon experience the benefits.

V : How to Create Your Happiness Lifestyle

I have taken you on quite a journey in this book.

We started off by gaining some understanding of how the brain works, processing thoughts and emotions and beyond. We learned how stress can impact our physical and mental well-being and how traumatic experiences can influence not only our present but also our future.

Then we moved on to explore the mind-body connection and learned about the relevance of nutrition and movement when it comes to our Happiness Frequency.

In the previous chapter, 'Training your Happiness Muscle', we explored how we can create a mindset shift to help us achieve our desired changes.

As we are nearing the end of this book, I wanted to equip you with a few more practical tools, tips, and resources to set you off to the best possible start. All of these exercises are tried and tested and have helped many of my clients develop sustainable lifestyle changes. But please remember: they will only work if you do them.

Creating an emotional connection to our goals

At the onset of the pandemic, I observed a lot of my clients struggling with the uncertainty of the situation. Not surprising, you might think. Yet, the people I was working with were mostly in an environment where they were still safe, had job security, were healthy, and didn't have to worry about family members and their health and well-being. It was merely the change in their everyday routines that upset their mental health so dramatically. By the way, I also had very few clients with children during this time, as they were too busy coping with home-schooling and their children's well-being. I searched research publications to find answers to the phenomenon of decreased resilience, but, of course, could not find anything that covered a similar situation to the pandemic. What I was able to find, and investigate a lot, was how people respond when they are in extreme crisis circumstances and exposed to life-threatening dangers.

In these cases, we tend to switch into survival mode. We deal, cope, and manage until the immediate danger is over, which is when we might experience post-traumatic stress disorder. In 2020, that was not the case for my clients. They were simply subjected to a dramatic change in their routines, their 'normal', and were confronted with a lot of uncertainty about the future. Remember how initially we were all talking about the 'new normal'? But this new normal never came, as everything continued to change. No two countries were taking the same approach, and even within countries, there were different regulations. We were exposed to prolonged periods of stress without time to recover and take ourselves out of the fight-or-flight response. But what was so stressful about the uncertainty?

The pandemic highlighted an important fact:

Most of us are not guided by our intentions and dreams, but merely react to circumstances!

Without goals, we are drifting through life without any sense of direction. Goals are like the lighthouse in a storm – you can see it, you know the direction, and even if it might be difficult to sail through a storm, you have faith, determination, and a path. In case of a dramatic event, such as the pandemic, you might have to correct your course, you might have to navigate around the epicenter of the storm. But you are still certain about where it is you want to go.

Many of us, however, live our lives chasing a variety of false goals that have been externally devised and suggested. From early childhood, we learn what is expected of us, what we might get appreciated for and what fits into social norms. We might be lucky enough to reach these goals, but only to then realize that we are still not happy or not feeling satisfied. If there is a dramatic change in our environment and circumstances, we don't have a lighthouse and we no longer know where to go. We are simply depending on and reacting to whatever life throws at us, rather than actively controlling the course of our lives.

You might have attended workshops or read about goal setting in the past. There is certainly a lot of important and valid information in these courses and books that you can draw upon whenever you are setting and defining any kind of personal or professional goals. Maybe you have heard of, or tried, the SMART goal-setting technique, which provides a handy framework for the definition of realistic and achievable goals.

S pecific   What outcome would you like?

M easurable   How will you know when you have reached it?

A ttainable   How confident do you feel that you will do it?

R elevant   How meaningful is this goal to you?

T imed   When do you intend to reach your endpoint?

If you are following the SMART technique, or similar, then you have taken a big step toward thoughtfully defining a relevant goal.

But the bad news is, no matter how SMART your goal is, you are quite likely to quit on the way. Or you might reach your goal, but within a short period of time lose all the progress you made to get there. Statistics have shown that around 39% of people tend to give up on their New Year's resolutions within the first month. Most of the remaining people quit within two years. Only around 5% of people stick to their goals with a long-lasting impact.

Whilst most research is done around goals that are taken for the beginning of a new year; we can probably safely assume that goals set during other times of the year are prone to experience the same outcome – failure. Whether the goal is a lifestyle change, a habit that we wish to incorporate, a specific attitude or mindset we aim to develop, a weight loss goal, improvement in diet or health habits, we struggle to stick to it. Throughout my career, I have watched and supported many clients starting off motivated and determined. Then, over time, come to depend more and more on me for motivation and follow-through. Many of my clients' reasons were that 'life happened' (doesn't it always?) and that's why they lost track and stopped their routine, whether this was in fitness or life coaching. Some, of course, made it, without hiccups, to their defined goal point. However, fast forward several months and most had lost some or all of their progress.

Does this sound familiar?

I have concluded that we take too simple an approach when it comes to goal setting. We are often swayed by an idea of what we should be doing and goals we should be aiming for. We see what our friends are doing, get influenced by social media or celebrities, and go with what seems to make sense.

When we *think* about our goals, we naturally use a rational, logical approach.

Example: 'I gained some pounds over the last few years; I will start an exercise program to get back in shape.'

If we follow the SMART principle, we might take our goal to the next level:

'I will lose ten pounds in six months by exercising for 60 minutes three times per week at XXX gym and follow a strict diet six days a week.'

This sounds great, right? All that we need to do now is to stick to the plan and we are quite certain to achieve our goal in less than six months! By the way, most goals are theoretically easy to achieve. But you probably already guessed that there is a high chance the story won't have this happy ending. So, let's go back to the beginning. Rather than 'think' about the goal, let us try to emotionally connect with it. As we've seen in previous chapters, emotions are powerful influencers on our internal world. Now, we're going to use them to help propel us in the direction we want to go.

Read the example below to better understand the path to emotional goal connection.

Example:

Goal: 'I want to get back in shape.'

Ask 'why' at least three times to discover the true point of urgency and the emotional connection.

Why is this important?

Example answer: *'Because I gained some extra weight.'*

Why does this matter?

'The extra weight might affect my health!'

Why do you want to improve your health?

'I want to stay active and healthy to be able to spend quality time with my family!'

➢ That is emotional motivator #1!

What are other reasons for why your weight bothers you?

'My clothes don't fit.'

How does that make you feel?

'I don't feel comfortable or attractive.'

➢ That is emotional motivator #2!

NEW, refined goal: 'I want to become more active and stay healthy for my family. I want to feel attractive and comfortable in my body.'

Note: none of the above can be measured by weight loss on a scale.

'Getting into shape' or 'losing weight' are simple examples that many of you might relate to; however, you can use this formula for any goal you might have. Can you see how the emotional connection gives the goal much more urgency? When we do not emotionally connect to our goal, then there are often no consequences if we do not achieve it. If the goal is simply to lose ten pounds, then not losing it might be frustrating, but will not be too important. However, if we are aware of the result of failure to our emotional goal (health, family, etc.), then we are much more likely to succeed.

Another important benefit of this technique is that our plan and program will be much more specific and tailored to our goal. In our example, we might now choose to scrap the gym and instead add fun activities that include the whole family. Maybe a few online seminars about healthy eating approaches can be watched together. Maybe this positive lifestyle change can even be tackled as a family affair and benefit everyone. In addition, we can add measures to deal with the insecurities that have become apparent.

Now it's your turn to give it a try.

Pick any goal you might have and ask a series of questions until you reach a goal with a truly emotional connection.

Don't be surprised if your new goal sounds different to the original one!

Goal:

(Ask 'why' at least three times.)

What is your motivator/are your motivators?

What is the final, emotionally-connected goal?

A long time ago, when I started to notice the worrying trend of quitting in my clients, I focused on changing my language to be more supportive during those periods when my clients were struggling and losing their motivation. I would teach and preach that it is normal to get off track, but that the important part was to get back on. This is something that I still believe to be a crucial skill. Yes, life happens – that's what life is meant to do. Picking back up where you left off is a significant talent to have. The more you align your lifestyle with your Happiness Frequency, the easier it gets to get back on track, simply because it has become your new, normal way of living and you are aware of the benefits and how good you feel because of it. You are also far less likely to let 'life get in the way' if you are truly emotionally connected to your goals and intentions. Because if you are, your goals become your life's mission. You will go through a beautiful mindset shift, from experiencing your path as a chore to feeling energized and fueled by your journey toward achievement!

Little trolls

You know the proverbial 'voice in your head'? That sudden whisper giving you all kinds of unhelpful, mean, and unsolicited advice? The voice comes from subconscious emotions that are important to discover and be aware of, as they might compromise your success. Imagine them as little trolls that appear, uninvited and often unnoticed, to sabotage your journey toward achieving your goals.

These trolls are often called **Fear**, **Self-doubt**, **Self-hatred,** and **Low Self-esteem,** but they can have many more names. These nasty emotions creep in and cause us to give up; they make us believe that we are doomed to fail. If you don't gain awareness of your trolls, they will come up with excuses. You might find yourself beginning to think: 'Who cares if I lose that weight?' or 'Many people around me are heavier than me and they are just fine!'

However, if you are aware of your trolls, you can respond with something like: 'I am scared to fail, but my goal is important to me because [insert emotional connection], and I will achieve it!'

Your turn!

Take a moment to define some of your trolls.

What are they called and when do they like to show up?

3 steps to reaching your goals

Once you've found what lights you up, what gets you excited, and what has real importance to you, it is time to fully commit. Remember that this is your story, and you are in the driver's seat; this also means that only you can make it happen! Unfortunately, only you can take full control of your thoughts, your actions, and the resulting emotional experience of your life. Fortunately, I think you'll soon find this 'unfortunate' fact to be an empowering truth.

Follow the three simple steps outlined below to follow through on goals of all sorts, whether physical, personal, mental, professional, or other.

Clarity

Be clear and precise about your goals! Now you know how to create an emotional connection to your goals and can make sure that you are passionate about and committed to them. Give yourself time to imagine the emotional outcome once you have reached your finish line. How will you feel? How will the achievement of this goal change your experiences? How will it impact other areas of your life? What will you gain?

Commitment

Fully subscribe to your goals and let go of fears and self-sabotaging actions! Become fully aware of anything and everything that may hold you back. Get to know your little trolls and kick them out of your life; disarm them. Consciously engage in actions that serve your journey. With everything you do, every response, every event, ask, 'does this get me closer to my goal?'

Redirection

Decide if your current actions are getting you to where you want to be; if not, redirect your energy! This is an ongoing action and questioning process to keep you moving in the right direction. Remember the train analogy from 'Our thoughts create our reality'? Make sure you are on the right train and traveling to the right station. If not, jump off! Now!

☞ **Exercise:**

Practice the steps above with your newly developed, emotionally-connected goal! Be clear, precise, committed, and analyze the need for redirection.

Clarity – what is your precise goal and why is it important?

Commitment – what actions/beliefs are taking you to your goal; what can you commit to?

Redirection – where do you need to redirect your energy and what will you no longer engage in?

✶ **Key points:**

- ✶ Goal setting: Goal setting can essentially be summed up as building our own personal lighthouse. When stress or other changes come into our lives, we have these foundational goals set within ourselves that can guide us moving in the direction we want to be moving.
- ✶ Rational vs emotional goal setting: Many people set goals that don't end up sticking. The trick is to find your personal relationship with your goal. What is at stake? What does it mean if the goal is not met? What does it

mean if the goal is met? By properly understanding how your goals will enrich you and your life, you establish an emotional connection with your goals, making it far more likely that you stick with them.

* Acknowledging our trolls and staying on the right train: Of course, even if we have a firm, emotional connection with our goals, there may still be moments when fear or self-doubt might come, in the form of stories we tell ourselves ('who really cares if I achieve this?'). However, if we can identify our trolls for what they are – trolls – we can stay headed toward our lighthouse.

Being eu-phoric, rather than eu-stressed!

I have worked with clients and coachees of different ages, backgrounds, and professions. Not all, but certainly many of them questioned why they were not feeling satisfied with what they had achieved. Even in their own subjective opinion, they saw no reason to be unhappy and depressed, but they weren't able to experience the satisfaction of their successes. Of course, we learned in the last chapter how we can prevent this by creating an emotional connection to our goals. However, a big chunk of my clientele consists of people that theoretically have ticked off most of their goals, like financial security, the house, the job, the car, the family. Yet they still found themselves asking, 'now what?'

Because they don't have an answer, they then continue doing what they know best, working hard and long hours and chasing a little more of everything they already have. Until, finally, they have to acknowledge their mental and physical stress symptoms. On their long tedious journey toward burnout, my clients sometimes try to escape their boredom, looking for something to excite them and give them an adrenaline rush. Remember that we can get easily addicted to stress hormones, and even if we are experiencing chronic stress, our minds and bodies might need higher doses to feel alive. To make this a little more complicated, not all stress is bad stress.

Eu-stress is a state of stress that is beneficial for our productivity and that keeps us in the state of 'flow'. We experience it when we are feeling confident, equipped to manage the tasks ahead, and when our work is aligned with our goals and the direction we want to take for our lives. The problem with eu-stress is that it is not sustainable and, like any form of stress, should be interspersed by times of mental rest and downtime. If prolonged, eu-stress will turn into regular chronic stress, with all its health complications. Because we no longer experience the satisfaction that was present when we were in the initial eu-stress phase, we can begin to feel bored and crave to get the positive 'stress-high'.

One of my coachees, a successful family father of three, confided to needing regular adventure holidays to give him something to look forward to. He told me that he only felt alive when he was engaging in risky activities, such as skydiving. Spending quality time with his children and wife, all of whom he loved dearly, often left him feeling drained and empty, which, in turn, brought a huge sensation of guilt. To avoid this horrible, nagging feeling, he started to withdraw and avoid the relaxing weekend activities his wife would propose. On top of this, another way of inducing positive emotions was through work, and so my client was chasing the big projects, throwing himself headfirst into countless hours on the job. The perfect example of a stress junkie and the negative effect this can have on our social life.

Of course, his is not an unusual story. In fact, I have heard this, and many variations of the same narrative, repeatedly. So why do so many of us fall into this trap?

Our minds and our brains need excitement as much as we need relaxation and rest. It is the healthy balance that we should be aiming to achieve. However, rather than going from excitement to peaceful rest, we go from chronic stress to exhaustion!

As we grow up, we are told to focus on our studies, get a job that helps us climb the career ladder, and, well, grow up. This leads most of us to, sooner or later, give up on our hobbies and free-time activities that used to excite us and bring us joy, allowing us to keep up with busy work schedules and tedious life tasks. Worryingly, even when I work with teenagers now, I can see a decline in the amount of extra-curricular activities they take part in. I am not suggesting that every child should have a packed schedule of (expensive) extra-curricular activities, but they should have a variety of hobbies, things they love doing that enable them to develop their social, emotional, physical, spiritual, and intellectual abilities. Then, as they grow older, they should aim to find a way to continue some of these activities into their adulthood. When did it become a written law that adults cannot have hobbies?

You might remember the chapter on neuroplasticity and how we can improve our brain's ability to adapt and create new neurological pathways by engaging in new activities, as well as by simply playing and having fun.

☞ Exercise:

Let's assess your engagement in activities that you might find exciting.

Answer the following questions:

- Which of your regular activities helps you to develop socially, emotionally, physically, spiritually, and intellectually?
- How much time per week do you spend learning new skills/gaining new knowledge/engaged in a hobby?
- What hobbies did you have when you were younger?
- What was it about these activities that you loved so much, e.g., playing in a team, the physical aspect, winning, learning, etc.?
- What used to bring you joy, happiness, and excitement when you were younger?
- What is something that you always wanted to do or learn, and why?

Based on your reflections, what is an activity or event that you can schedule and plan RIGHT NOW that will fill you with excitement, euphoria, and joy?

Make a commitment – now – to bring the fun back into your life!

Start quitting!

Emotionally healthy people are quitters! They have learned to stop engaging in a long list of behaviors and activities that don't serve their physical, mental, and spiritual well-being. Equally important to adding euphoria is to actively eliminate stressors. We need to be mindful of our eu-stress and ensure that we have a good balance of stress and rest.

I'll be the first to admit that, for me personally, this is a difficult concept. I am stubborn, I am persistent, I don't do 'patience', and I certainly don't quit! I get things done. I persevere. I hustle. I have been in many situations and interpersonal relationships in my life that were not adding anything but stress, and yet I could not quit. Because I am strong and I can handle the pressure.

But here is my new life motto:

Just because you can, does not mean you should!

Hopefully, you are a lot smarter than me and you are calling BS on my, and maybe your own, behavior right now.

As individuals and societies, we must move away from the hustle culture and move toward a softer and much more accommodating mindset that maintains integrity with the values of self-care and self-love, even during high-stress times.

My big dream is a world in which it is ok to drop everything and share with those around us that we are feeling overwhelmed. A world in which it is ok to quit trying to do everything alone and ask for help. A world that not only accepts emotional vulnerability, but expects us to be open, upfront, and self-aware of our limitations.

That would be a world that produces a whole other type of generational wealth: emotional and mental health!

Energy vs Time Management

Time Management is a common topic of personal development courses offered in many organizations. In recent decades, our world has morphed into a 24/7 lifestyle environment and has forced us to become comfortable with multi-tasking, long workdays, unexpected meetings, tight deadlines, and the need to always be available.

How can we manage our time with the continuous, increasing stream of ongoing tasks? Do you feel that your 'to-do list' never seems completed? Does it seem that the celebration of achievements is constantly overshadowed by a never-ending backlash of work? It appears that the demand and expectation of always being 'on' leads us to continue to add more and more to our plate.

With many of my clients, I've noticed the desire to manage their time more effectively. The topic of 'time management' is brought up often. I am sure many of you have thought the famous thought, 'There is just not enough time in the day'. We all know that time is finite. There are only 24 hours in a day, out of which we need to get a healthy amount of sleep, spend time eating and drinking, take care of waste removal, and ideally live a little. So, realistically, we do not manage time. Time is just there, it is not influenced by us whatsoever, and we have no control over it.

But what we do manage is what we do in these 1,440 minutes and how we feel about what we do. The actual tasks should be filtered through the more traditional 'time management' skills and be analyzed for their need and usefulness. This enables us to be more efficient and effective. If you would like to get some quite radical ideas on how to streamline your tasks, I recommend reading 'The 4-hour work week', by Tim Ferriss.

Energy Management, on the other hand, considers the way we feel energetically during our day.

When analyzing a given task or activity, there are two big considerations:

1. How is my energy right now?
2. Does this task/activity refill or drain my energy?

Our overall energy is highly influenced by our lifestyle. As we have learned in the previous chapters, how we eat, our exercise and movement habits, our sleep, and, of course, our stress levels are all closely connected to how energetic, balanced, and rested we feel.

We are all painfully aware of the many things we have to do that drain our energy. These might be boring, tedious tasks we must do; annoying people we have to deal with; work in general; being stuck in traffic; not having enough time for ourselves; and so on. We cannot eliminate all the tasks that drain our energy, but we can make sure to add activities that fill our energy up to maintain a positive balance.

One exercise I do with all my clients is to let them take stock of their 'energy bank account'.

☞ Exercise:

Your energy bank account

Step one:

Make two lists of 15 activities/tasks each – one listing the things that drain you and one for the things that refill you.

Step two:

Write a detailed list of activities you do daily and mark them with a 'plus' if you find the activity refilling, 'minus' if draining, or keep blank when neutral. If your days are quite varied, you might have to do this once for every day of the week. Next, note down how you perceive the quality of your energy overall.

Note: Some activities that you might think are neutral can be positive or negative, depending on the thoughts and emotional experiences you have whilst doing them. For example, getting ready in the morning. I often feel rushed and stressed in the morning, so these become draining activities.

Step three:

What is your energy balance?

What can you commit to, right now, to improve it?

Assess your daily activities (from step two) and find ways to turn draining experiences into refilling experiences. Take a look at the first step to find activities that recharge your energy.

Below is a sample schedule from one of my clients for one specific day of the week:

5:30 Wake up and check phone in bed +

5:45 Get up and get ready −

6:15 Wake up children and help them get ready −

6:45 Breakfast –

7:15 Drive kids to school and then to work +/ – (depends on the day, mood of the kids, traffic)

8:00 Arrive at work, get a coffee, chat with colleagues +

8:30 Work – (sometimes + in between, but generally stressed)

12:00 Lunch – /+ (if time then +, often rushed, skip lunch)

13:00 Work –

17:00 Leave Work + (if I am late to leave work then –)

17:30 Gym +

19:00 Home – (normally complaints about being late, kids needing something, feels rushed and I feel guilty)

20:00 Dinner +

21:00 TV – (not really enjoying myself most times, interrupted by work emails, can't relax)

22:30 Bed – (struggle to fall asleep most days)

In the case of my client above, we made a few adjustments in several stages. We worked on work-related issues and created a different energy at work after some time, but the immediate changes that were implemented were:

Get up and get ready – listening to motivational podcasts or audiobooks.

Lunch – prep meals during the weekend and bring to work.

Home – dedicated quality time with kids, different activities each day, e.g., games night, cooking together, going for a walk, etc.

TV – Replaced with reading time, phone switched off from 19:00 hrs.

Bed – improved because of reading time/downtime.

Another helpful exercise can be paying attention to, and becoming more aware of, the fluctuation of your energy levels throughout your day. This can be useful to avoid scheduling tasks that require high focus and concentration during the times that you might feel less sharp. It can also help you find the most suitable time for workouts and guide the way you eat. However, this only works if you have some flexibility and control over your schedule and are not too preoccupied. It's great knowing that you are naturally a night owl, but this doesn't do you any good if, for whatever reason, you need to get up at 5:30 am.

One of the most important acts of self-love is to be more mindful and conscious about our energy management, our stress levels, and the amount of excitement and happiness in our daily life. As we get older, our responsibilities increase and our duties and pressures can pile high. That's when we need to go the extra mile to engage in healthy activities that make us feel alive and bring us laughter and joy. If we miss this conscious step, then our subconscious mind might lead us toward destructive, unhealthy, and damaging thought patterns, behaviors, and stress cycles.

✱ Key points:

- ✱ Stress revisited – riding the flow vs getting addicted to it: When one is well equipped to handle a certain situation and feels capable of getting through it, they may experience a form of stress known as eu-stress. This type of stress can help us achieve a flow state, allowing us to achieve the task in front of us. However, even eu-stress needs to be balanced with times of rest and relaxation. If this is not done, eu-stress can eventually turn into chronic stress.

- ✱ Bringing hobbies back into adult life: As we get older, we tend to drop sports and other recreational activities for the sake of work and other life needs. However, reintroducing activities that we love can be a great source of joy and relaxation.

- ✱ Time and energy management – auditing our energy bank accounts: This chapter contains an exercise to help us identify what activities we're spending our time on and how these activities make us feel (recharged or drained). Once these are identified, we can start to tweak, and maybe replace, certain activities so our days feel more charging and less energy-demanding.

The 3-month bucket list

The happiness muscle is a lot like other muscles in our body. Once you start training it, it only gets stronger and stronger. Like with physical training, we might experience setbacks, go through episodes of stress and trauma and some of the more uncomfortable feelings. But it's still there, and in the end, we are designed to use it and tune back into our Happiness Frequency.

Training your happiness muscle really is like training any other muscle. Consistency is key, but we also want to train smart! The #1 reason people don't stick to their physical exercise program is because they set themselves up for failure by being too aggressive with their training, setting their expectations too high in regard to the frequency and duration of their sessions, take an 'all-or-nothing' approach, or some combination of the three. The same accounts for training our happiness muscle, or mindset. The reality is that you will have days when you are feeling low, when you cannot get yourself motivated to work on your mindset, and when the world simply seems gloomy and doomed. And this is ok. You need to learn to be ok with it and listen to your mind and body.

Our intrinsic tendency to want to be perfect at everything we set out to do might actually be one of the reasons we are stressed out in the first place. Tapping into our Happiness Frequency means accepting a slower pace, enjoying the process, and not perceiving the practice as a chore. The moment you think a thought like 'I have to do this' or 'I should do this', you already lost the battle. Try to keep an observational approach, notice your feelings and emotions, and summarize them in a simple statement, such as, 'I am not feeling motivated today'. By owning the sensation, you are taking its power. You can then continue to explore any reward options that will enhance the notion of being ok with what you are feeling. This could be something like, 'I am not motivated today. I will treat myself later to a few minutes of my favorite music with a cup of tea.' Can you see how this, quite rational and unemotional, approach enables you to take ownership of the situation and might be beneficial to your mental health? There will be no punishment, no self-derogative speech, and no consequences – just acceptance.

It's so simple that you might have already used this tactic many times, but probably when advising others. We tend to be much kinder with those around us than we are with ourselves. If this is something you recognize in yourself, then practice thinking about the advice you would give to others first, before you beat yourself up over not accomplishing whatever you set out to do. Then simply give yourself the same guidance and treat yourself with the same kindness that you would extend to someone else. This is true self-love!

Developing our happiness muscle is essential to living a fulfilled life. However, it can be challenging to stay on track when life takes over and tries to keep us tied to our old, stressed, and overwhelmed mindset. The 3-month bucket list is a great method to avoid feeling plagued by the idea of 'forever'. You simply change your mindset from having to achieve something from now until the end of time and focus on a smaller, more achievable timeframe – the next three months! The purpose of this method is to provide a sense of purpose and accomplishment, while also fostering a positive mindset. By making sure that you achieve your tasks, no matter how small, you will positively impact your dopamine levels and the activity itself might trigger the release of your serotonin, oxytocin, and endorphins.

I regularly use this technique, especially when I know that I have a stressful time ahead of me and I want to prevent burnout and mental exhaustion. It is important that you are realistic with the timings and tasks, which is why it helps to schedule check-ins to allow for course corrections. Whilst I am writing the final chapters of this book, I have a clearly defined timeline that I want to adhere to. The previous stages of writing were more liberal, but I know that there will be other demanding projects coming up soon, hence I am scheduling myself more tightly as I approach the finish line. Therefore, my 3-month bucket list needs to support my mental health, as well as my physiological well-being during this 'crunch time'. I have a 10-min breathing exercise (Wim Hof, I highly recommend it for focus and concentration), that I treat myself to whenever I feel mentally drained. I schedule movement breaks (walking the dog and 15-minute Mini-Workouts), and I am eating well. That's it! There is never any need to overcomplicate things, we just want to keep it simple and achievable.

The 3-month bucket list also helps you to become aware of what does and does not actually work for you. There are a multitude of wellness programs, tools, techniques, and practices out there. The same accounts for exercise and nutrition. With this book, I am throwing all of it at you, all bundled together, and yes, it is a lot! I would be surprised if you haven't thought, at least once thus far, that this is just too much. It is … but it also isn't. Keep in mind that just because there are many things you could do, you certainly shouldn't do all of them. Remember that you are working toward a sustainable lifestyle change that you enjoy, and this will take a little bit of time and figuring out. Every time you automate a new behavior, it will move into your subconscious mind and you will no longer have to think or worry about it. The thoughts, feelings, and emotions that are connected to this new behavior will also become embedded in your subconscious, and all of this together will become who you are. You have created change! However, to do so we need to take it easy and one step at a time.

The 3-month bucket list method can help to develop a happiness mindset by providing a sense of direction and focus. When we have clear goals and activities to work toward, it can be easier to stay motivated and positive. This can help to reduce feelings of anxiety and stress, which can often lead to negative thoughts and emotions. Another benefit of this method is that it can promote a happiness mindset by encouraging us to step outside of our comfort zones. When we set goals and activities that challenge us, it can be a powerful way to build confidence and self-esteem. This can help to improve our overall mental health and well-being, which can lead to a more positive outlook on life.

Further, you might be more likely to try something outside of your comfort zone knowing that you are doing it within a limited time window.

In addition, the 3-month bucket list can help us to cultivate a sense of gratitude and appreciation. By including activities that bring us joy and happiness, we can learn to appreciate the simple things in life. This can help us to focus on the positive aspects of our lives, rather than dwelling on negative experiences. When I take my 10-minute breathing break, I appreciate myself for taking a break; I focus on the beautiful space I am in, the birds tweeting, my cat and dog giving me company, whatever works in that moment.

However, please note that the 3-month bucket list method does not work for everyone. If you find it difficult to set and achieve goals within a specific time frame or struggle with the pressure of meeting deadlines, then this might not be the right tool for you. Some of my clients prefer to work with a much shorter time frame, like a week, or even three days. Others succeed when they over-commit themselves, so that it doesn't matter when not everything gets accomplished. Self-development is an ongoing process that requires consistent effort and dedication. It involves setting goals, acquiring new skills, and improving oneself in various areas of life. More importantly, it requires self-awareness and being authentic and honest with ourselves. We constantly change; tools that work today might not work tomorrow, and vice versa. So give it a try, but don't worry if you are not feeling it. Even if it is not for you, this exercise might give you ideas for other exercises to try.

How to apply the 3-month bucket list:

- ✓ Identify your goals. What do you want to achieve within the next three months? Your goals could be personal, professional, or a combination of both. Make sure you focus on the emotional experience. Write them down and be specific. For instance, if you want to be more confident when you are public speaking, your goal could be to attend a public speaking course or to practice speaking in front of a mirror for 30 minutes every day.

- ✓ Break down your goals into smaller, achievable tasks. This will help you to stay motivated and focused. For instance, if your goal is to read a book every week, break it down into reading for 30 minutes every day. This makes the goal more manageable and less overwhelming.Prioritize your goals. Identify which goals are most important to you and focus on them first. This will help you to make progress and avoid feeling overwhelmed. For instance, if your goal is to learn a new language as well as to improve your fitness, prioritize the fitness goal first and then focus on learning the language. Not everything has to happen in one 3-month block.

- ✓ Track your progress AND adjust. This will help you to stay motivated and on track. Use a journal or a planner to track your progress and celebrate small wins along the way. Be honest with yourself if you have over-planned and make adjustments as needed.

- ✓ Be open to new experiences and challenges. This will help you to grow and learn new things. Don't be afraid to step out of your comfort zone and try something novel to you. This could be as simple as trying new foods or taking a dance class.

To make sure that your 3-month bucket list truly enables you to tune into your Happiness Frequency, there are a few helpful tools and practices that have been proven to increase mental well-being and happiness.

1. Practice gratitude: Gratitude is a powerful way to shift your focus from what you don't have to what you do have. Make a habit of expressing gratitude every day, whether it's through journaling, meditation, or simply taking a few moments to appreciate the good things in your life.

2. Cultivate positive relationships: Positive relationships are key to a happy life. Make time for the people who uplift and support you and let go of toxic relationships that drain your energy.

3. Engage in activities you enjoy: Engaging in activities that you enjoy is a great way to boost your mood and overall happiness. Whether it's playing a sport, painting, or listening to music, make time for activities that bring you joy.

4. Take care of your physical health: Taking care of your physical health is essential to overall happiness. Make sure you get enough sleep, eat a balanced diet, and regularly engage in physical activity.

5. Practice mindfulness: Mindfulness is the practice of being present in the moment and fully engaged in the task at

hand. By practicing mindfulness, you can reduce stress and increase overall happiness.

6. Set happiness goals and work toward them: Create specific happiness goals and work toward achieving them. For example, if you want to improve your mental health, you could set a goal to attend mindfulness workshops, coaching, or therapy once a week for three months.

7. Practice self-compassion: Self-compassion is the practice of treating yourself with kindness and understanding, rather than criticism and judgment. Cultivating self-compassion can lead to greater happiness and self-acceptance. Make a goal to practice self-compassion every day, whether it's through positive self-talk or treating yourself with kindness and understanding.

Creating a 3-month bucket list really is a great, simple, and enjoyable way to kickstart your self-development journey and train your happiness muscle. In addition, it is a tool that will be beneficial in many different stages of your life and will easily become second nature. By setting specific goals, breaking them down into achievable tasks, prioritizing them, tracking your progress, and being open to new experiences, you truly can achieve significant growth and development in just three months. You can adjust, change, and play with this method to make it fit your needs. Remember to stay focused, stay motivated, and enjoy the journey toward a happier lifestyle.

✳ Key points:

- ✳ What is the 3-month bucket list plan: The 3-month bucket list is a great method to avoid feeling plagued by the idea of 'forever'. You simply change your mindset from having to achieve something from now until the end of time, and focus on a smaller, more achievable timeframe – the next three months!

- ✳ How to stay on task and avoid burnout and/or feeling overwhelmed: The purpose of this method is to provide a sense of purpose and accomplishment while also fostering a positive mindset. By making sure that you achieve your tasks, no matter how small, you will positively impact your dopamine levels, helping you to feel motivated.

- ✳ Tips for staying in tune with your Happiness Frequency as you pursue your goals: When in doubt, this chapter contains a list of exercises to help you continue to flex your happiness muscle and stay heading toward your goals.

Commit to the project of YOU!

The Wellness industry has exploded in the past decade, and, fortunately, more people than ever before are consciously subscribing to the idea of finding a lifestyle that makes them feel happier, more satisfied, fitter, and healthier. Long gone are the days when we were willing to accept that certain circumstances, such as becoming parents, working long hours, etc., should hold us back from feeling energetic and healthy – theoretically. In reality, however, we still often get sidetracked by life, family, and work and end up prioritizing everything but ourselves. In a world that seems to be spinning faster every single day, there is just not enough time, is there?

Many of the wellness exercises that are being suggested and promoted are indeed time-consuming and complicated. It seems that only those already dedicated to a healthy lifestyle can fully commit to the many techniques of biohacking & co – ice baths, water filters, yoga, meditation, complicated diets, specific supplementation, certain workout methods, metabolic tracking, glucose monitoring, bulletproof coffee, sleep monitoring, salt bath, sound healing, red light therapy. The list is endless!

Whilst I certainly appreciate the concept of biohacking, it is yet another example of looking into advanced techniques before having established a sustainable foundation. I have witnessed this in all areas of physical and mental health and well-being practices. Instead of learning how to eat a 'normal', well-balanced diet, we overeat and then engage in restrictive, complicated, and advanced diets. Rather than exploring the minimum amount of movement that we are comfortable with and that suffices to give us the desired benefits, we adopt an all-or-nothing mentality and beat ourselves up if our rigorous workout routine is not sustainable. Instead of finding short, yet effective, mini-mindfulness exercises that we can happily commit to, we believe that we must sit in uncomfortable positions for 30 minutes each day.

We turn what is supposed to make us feel better into challenging, punishing routines and are surprised when we don't persevere.

Finding balance

This book is about YOU tuning into YOUR Happiness Frequency, learning how to read your personal blueprint to allow you to do exactly this. There are no two people on this planet that will have the same blueprint to do so. I am sorry if this realization makes the title of the book feel a bit misleading, but I hope, as you are reaching the end of this book, you know that the true blueprint is the knowledge and the empowerment to make educated, informed decisions about which practices you want to consider and why. Whatever you choose to do after reading the last page, let it be guided by your intuition and the awareness of what will make you happy. Then, only as a second step, use the knowledge you have gained to decide on your specific plan of action. Be aware that this action plan is always going to be a work in progress. Whatever works for you right now might not work in six months, for whatever reason. And that is ok!

Like this book, life is not linear, with no clear starting point, no set trajectory; it is continuous growth. As we have learned, our bodies and minds are constantly changing, as are our circumstances. But throughout life's wonderful, messy, raw journey, let's remember the importance of staying true to our goals and staying committed to the project of your Happiness.

Now go and write your story....

About Created Coaching

As I was finishing up this book, I suddenly realized that I didn't remember when I decided to write it. In my memory, there was the time before I wrote it and then, suddenly, I was doing it. It certainly wasn't something I'd always dreamt of doing, and the process was quite challenging. I had become familiar with academic writing during my master's program but writing the 'Happiness Frequency' was entirely different. Even though it is about my coaching method, it felt personal and surprisingly intimate. This is probably because who I am as a person and my business are tightly intertwined and I absolutely love what I do.

There have been many courses, studies, people, and situations that have influenced my work over the years and shaped my opinion about physical and mental health interventions. Of course, from the early beginnings of Created Coaching in 2020, I truly believed in my approach. But initially, it took some time to position myself amongst other coaches and wellness providers because of the complexity of my programs and the wide applications of my holistic approach. Some people couldn't quite connect the dots between me doing yoga with horses, offering corporate leadership programs, working with children in schools, running a retreat in Zanzibar, and much more – all within a couple of months.

However, I knew that offering this variety of programs, covering all the areas that I consider necessary, was the only possible way for me to work. I didn't want to narrow my services down to make it easier for my clients to put me into a box. My 'niche' was never a specific target audience or a specific service but, rather, people that are ready to take ownership and responsibility of their own journey and to commit to a healthier and happier mind and body. To this day, I struggle with my elevator pitch; I am so passionate about giving knowledge, empowering people to make their own informed decisions, and showing them that they have choices that I just can't seem to sum it up in 30 seconds.

Maybe this book can be my exceedingly lengthy elevator pitch – if someone got stuck with me in an elevator overnight. Jokes aside, everything you have in this book is relevant to the Created Coaching methodology. When I work with my clients, I aim to assess their lifestyle, encourage them to optimize their hormonal balance through nutrition and movement, help them manage their stress levels, and, eventually, tune into their Happiness Frequency. I have done it many, many times.

I know that this approach works if you, dear reader, are ready to commit and make the change.

Truly yours,

Tash Enriquez

📷 created.coaching

🌐 created-coaching.com

✉ tash@created-coaching.com

in Natascha Enriquez

About the Author

Natascha (Tash) Enriquez has facilitated and curated educational wellness and coaching experiences for over 17 years. After her first degree in Fitness Management, Tash continued to further her own education, achieving a postgraduate diploma in Sports and Exercise Science and Medicine. Tash has established the Sport & Wellness Science Lab at New York University Abu Dhabi, where she conducted research in the areas of neuroscience, sport psychology and wellness.

She is an ICF-certified Life Coach (Results Certified Coaching and Organizational Relationships and Systems Coach) a certified Horse-Guided Empowerment Facilitator, an established consultant, speaker, and coach.

Tash's coaching business, Created Coaching, focuses on education about physiological principles, mindset changes, and self-empowerment. She is passionate about enabling individuals to create their own path to an improved lifestyle and to find their unique Happiness Frequency.

Tash lives with her son, cat, and dog in Abu Dhabi. Her favorite moments are spent outdoors with her son and friends, either relaxing or enjoying some activities together, such as ice-skating, jet-skiing, or wake-boarding. She greatly values time in nature, by the sea, and with the horses which she is also fortunate to use in her coaching sessions and Leadership Trainings.

Acknowledgements

This book would have never happened if it wasn't for the support and cheerleading of many people and some animals.

Firstly, my son Akin, who is my greatest inspiration to become a better, happier human every single day. Watching you being this unbelievably smart little person reminds me that we truly hold all the answers and wisdom inside! I love you to infinity.

I have been so fortunate to meet amazing people at NYU Abu Dhabi who encouraged me to follow my areas of interest and gave me space and support to grow professionally in ways I never thought possible. You have uplifted me beyond the academic field.

A big 'Thank you' to my many clients who regularly share updates about their journeys and send me very kind messages of gratitude and encouragement – always surprising, and always in the perfect moments. Your trust is a very special gift. I learn through you, and I grow because of you.

Writing this book has been full of learnings, and I was very lucky to have the best people assisting me. My editor,

Phoenix Raig, has been a wonderful teacher on this journey. I am so grateful for your feedback and thorough assessment and corrections of my manuscript.

Thank you to my friends, who have held the space and time for me to write, do my thing, and have cheered me on. I really learned the value of people who can show up to celebrate you and with you in this process!

My dear Alvaro, my angel horse… I have no words to describe our time together. But you know, and we never needed words. Run wild and free. Until we meet again.

Finally, Mokka and Kenny, the two sweetest pets in the world, who are the best company anyone can have – I love you.

Printed in Great Britain
by Amazon